Reteaching Workbook

TAKE ANOTHER LOOK

TEACHER'S EDITION
Grade 3

Harcourt Brace & Company

Orlando • Atlanta • Austin • Boston • San Francisco • Chicago • Dallas • New York • Toronto • London

http://www.hbschool.com

CONTENTS

Addition Strategies

You can **make a ten** to help you find sums.

---

9 + 5 = ?   **Think:** 5 = 1 + 4

- First, add 1 to 9 to make 10.
- Then, add 4 to 10 to make 14.

    9 + 5 = 10 + 4

    9 + 5 = 14

● ● ● ● ● ● ● ● ● ○
○ ○ ○ ○

---

7 + 4 = ?   **Think:** 4 = 3 + 1

- First, add 3 to 7 to make 10.
- Then, add 1 to 10 to make 11.

    7 + 4 = 10 + 1

    7 + 4 = 11

● ● ● ● ● ● ● ○ ○ ○
○

Write the missing addend.

1. 9 + _1_ = 10   2. 7 + _3_ = 10   3. 8 + _2_ = 10

Find the sum. Draw counters to show how you made a ten.
Check students' drawings.

4. 8 + 6 = _14_   5. 3 + 9 = _12_

6. 8 + 4 = _12_   7. 5 + 7 = _12_

8. 4 + 9 = _13_   9. 3 + 8 = _11_

10. 2 + 9 = _11_   11. 7 + 3 = _10_

More Addition Strategies

When both addends are the same, you are adding **doubles.**
When you add doubles, the sum is always *even.*

Find the sum of these doubles.

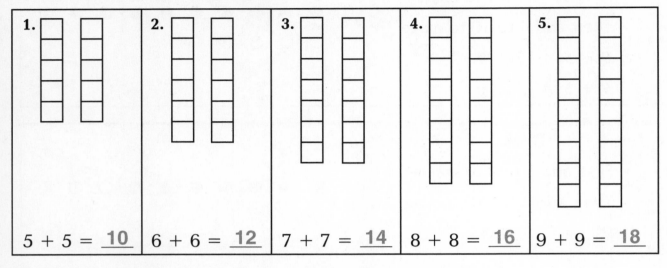

1.	2.	3.	4.	5.
5 + 5 = 10	6 + 6 = 12	7 + 7 = 14	8 + 8 = 16	9 + 9 = 18

When one addend is *one more* than the other, add the
doubles and then add one more to the sum. The sum is
always *odd.*

Use what you know about adding doubles. Find the sum of
these doubles plus one.

6.	7.	8.	9.	10.
5 + 5 = 10	8 + 8 = 16	7 + 7 = 14	4 + 4 = 8	6 + 6 = 12
5 + 6 = 11	8 + 9 = 17	7 + 8 = 15	4 + 5 = 9	6 + 7 = 13
6 + 6 = 12	9 + 9 = 18	8 + 8 = 16	5 + 5 = 10	7 + 7 = 14

LESSON
1.3

Order and Zero

Numbers may be added in any order. The sum is the same.

● ● ●   ○ ○

  3   +   2   =   5

  ○ ○   ● ● ●

  2   +   3   =   5

When **0** is added to any number, the sum is that number.

● ● ● ● ● ●

6 + 0 = 6
0 + 6 = 6

Find the sum. You may use counters.

1. 9   8
   + 8   + 9
   ___   ___
   17   17

2. 6   8
   + 8   + 6
   ___   ___
   14   14

3. 9   2
   + 2   + 9
   ___   ___
   11   11

4. 0   4
   + 4   + 0
   ___   ___
   4   4

5. 7   6
   + 6   + 7
   ___   ___
   13   13

6. 3   8
   + 8   + 3
   ___   ___
   11   11

7. 6   0
   + 0   + 6
   ___   ___
   6   6

8. 6   5
   + 5   + 6
   ___   ___
   11   11

9. 0   7
   + 7   + 0
   ___   ___
   7   7

10. 7   8
    + 8   + 7
    ___   ___
    15   15

11. 9   5
    + 5   + 9
    ___   ___
    14   14

12. 0   5
    + 5   + 0
    ___   ___
    5   5

13. 4 + 8 = __12__

8 + 4 = __12__

14. 9 + 3 = __12__

3 + 9 = __12__

15. 8 + 0 = __8__

0 + 8 = __8__

16. 4 + 3 = __7__

3 + 4 = __7__

17. 7 + 3 = __10__

3 + 7 = __10__

18. 0 + 9 = __9__

9 + 0 = __9__

Write the missing number.

19. 4 + 5 = __5__ + 4

20. 9 + 7 = __7__ + 9

21. 4 + 3 = 3 + __4__

22. 3 + 6 = __6__ + 3

23. 5 + 8 = 8 + __5__

24. 9 + 1 = 1 + __9__

Problem-Solving Strategy

Make a Table

The following table shows all the number sentences
that can be made using the numbers 7–9 as addends.

Number Sentences		
7 + 7 = 14	8 + 7 = 15	9 + 7 = 16
7 + 8 = 15	8 + 8 = 16	9 + 8 = 17
7 + 9 = 16	8 + 9 = 17	9 + 9 = 18

There are many patterns in this table.

• Look for number sentences in which both addends
are the same.

• Look for pairs of number sentences that have the
same addends in a different order.

1. Complete the table to show all the number sentences
that can be made using the numbers 3–6 as addends.
Follow the pattern that has been started.

Number Sentences			
3 + 3 = <u>6</u>	4 + 3 = <u>7</u>	5 + 3 = <u>8</u>	<u>6 + 3 = 9</u>
3 + 4 = <u>7</u>	4 + 4 = <u>8</u>	<u>5 + 4 = 9</u>	<u>6 + 4 = 10</u>
3 + 5 = <u>8</u>	<u>4 + 5 = 9</u>	<u>5 + 5 = 10</u>	<u>6 + 5 = 11</u>
<u>3 + 6 = 9</u>	<u>4 + 6 = 10</u>	<u>5 + 6 = 11</u>	<u>6 + 6 = 12</u>

2. Use the table from Problem 1. List 3 pairs of number sentences that have the same addends in a different order.
There are 6 possible answers.

<u>   3 + 4 = 7   </u> and <u>   4 + 3 = 7   </u> or 4 + 5 = 9 and 5 + 4 = 9

<u>   3 + 5 = 8   </u> and <u>   5 + 3 = 8   </u>   4 + 6 = 10 and 6 + 4 = 10

<u>   3 + 6 = 9   </u> and <u>   6 + 3 = 9   </u>   5 + 6 = 11 and 6 + 5 = 11

Name _____

LESSON
1.4

Subtraction Strategies

You can subtract to compare two numbers.

To **count up,** begin with the smaller number and count up to the larger number.

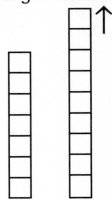

Count: 7 . . . 8, 9

So, 9 − 7 = 2.

To **count back,** begin with the larger number and count back 1, 2, or 3 to the smaller number.

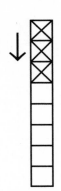

Count: 8 . . . 7, 6, 5

So, 8 − 3 = 5.

Find the difference. You may use counters.

1. 7 − 2 = __5__

2. 9 − 8 = __1__

3. 10 − 8 = __2__

4. 12 − 3 = __9__

5. 11 − 3 = __8__

6. 7 − 6 = __1__

7. 13 − 11 = __2__

8. 6 − 4 = __2__

9. 18 − 3 = __15__

10. 11 − 9 = __2__

11. 7 − 5 = __2__

12. 8 − 2 = __6__

13. 5 − 3 = __2__

14. 10 − 7 = __3__

15. 15 − 2 = __13__

Find the difference. Ring *count up* or *count back*.

16.   9 (count up)
    − 6 count back
     ‾‾‾
      3

17.   5 count up
    − 1 (count back)
     ‾‾‾
      4

18.   8 count up
    − 2 (count back)
     ‾‾‾
      6

19.   9 (count up)
    − 7 count back
     ‾‾‾
      2

Harcourt Brace School Publishers

TAKE ANOTHER LOOK   R5

Fact Families

Each fact in a fact family uses
the same three numbers.

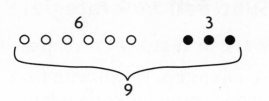

Look for the numbers 3, 6, and 9 in each fact in the table below.

Questions Using the Same Fact Family	Fact
Bill has 6 white marbles and 3 black marbles. How many marbles does Bill have in all?	$6 + 3 = 9$
Bill has 3 black marbles and 6 white marbles. How many marbles does Bill have in all?	$3 + 6 = 9$
Bill has 9 marbles. He has 3 black marbles and the rest are white. How many marbles are white?	$9 - 3 = 6$
Bill has 9 marbles. He has 6 white marbles and the rest are black. How many marbles are black?	$9 - 6 = 3$

Complete the fact family for each group of numbers.

1. 2, 8, 10

$2 + 8 = \underline{10}$

$8 + 2 = \underline{10}$

$10 - 2 = \underline{8}$

$10 - 8 = \underline{2}$

2. 9, 5, 14

$9 + 5 = \underline{14}$

$5 + 9 = \underline{14}$

$14 - 9 = \underline{5}$

$14 - 5 = \underline{9}$

3. 7, 6, 13

$7 + 6 = \underline{13}$

$6 + 7 = \underline{13}$

$13 - 7 = \underline{6}$

$13 - 6 = \underline{7}$

4. 8, 3, 11

$8 + 3 = \underline{11}$

$3 + 8 = \underline{11}$

$11 - 8 = \underline{3}$

$11 - 3 = \underline{8}$

5. 5, 7, 12

$5 + 7 = \underline{12}$

$7 + 5 = \underline{12}$

$12 - 5 = \underline{7}$

$12 - 7 = \underline{5}$

6. 4, 8, 12

$4 + 8 = \underline{12}$

$8 + 4 = \underline{12}$

$12 - 4 = \underline{8}$

$12 - 8 = \underline{4}$

More Than Two Addends

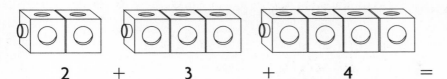

$$2 \quad + \quad 3 \quad + \quad 4 \quad = \quad ?$$

To find the sum of more than two addends, you can group the addends in different ways. The sum is always the same.

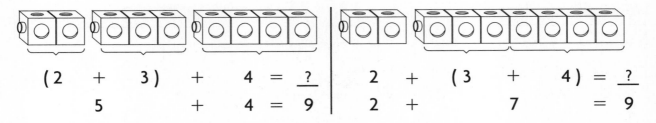

$(2 \ + \ 3) \ + \ 4 = \ ?$	$2 \ + \ (3 \ + \ 4) = \ ?$
$5 \quad + \quad 4 = 9$	$2 \ + \quad 7 \quad = 9$

Add the numbers in ( ) first. Then find the sum.

1. $(4 + 1) + 6 = \underline{?}$ **2.** $(3 + 2) + 8 = \underline{?}$ **3.** $(9 + 1) + 6 = \underline{?}$

$\quad \underline{5} + 6 = \underline{11}$ $\quad \underline{5} + 8 = \underline{13}$ $\quad \underline{10} + 6 = \underline{16}$

$4 + (1 + 6) = \underline{?}$ $3 + (2 + 8) = \underline{?}$ $9 + (1 + 6) = \underline{?}$

$4 + \underline{7} = \underline{11}$ $3 + \underline{10} = \underline{13}$ $9 + \underline{7} = \underline{16}$

Group the addends by drawing ( ). Then find the sum. **The placement of the parentheses will vary.**

4. $(5 + 5) + 4 = \underline{14}$ **5.** $3 + (4 + 6) = \underline{13}$ **6.** $(6 + 2) + 7 = \underline{15}$

7. $(3 + 7) + 2 = \underline{12}$ **8.** $3 + (8 + 2) = \underline{13}$ **9.** $(6 + 2) + 6 = \underline{14}$

10. $(6 + 4) + 7 = \underline{17}$ **11.** $(7 + 2) + 6 = \underline{15}$ **12.** $(9 + 1) + 2 = \underline{12}$

Find the sum.

13.	**14.**	**15.**	**16.**	**17.**
6	3	8	3	4
4	3	1	2	3
+3	+7	+9	+6	+5
13	**13**	**18**	**11**	**12**

Modeling Addition of Two-Digit Numbers

Sometimes you need to regroup 10 ones as 1 ten when you add.

Add 38 + 15.

Step 1 Add the ones. If there are 10 or more, regroup 10 ones to make a ten.

Tens	Ones
¹3	8
+ 1	5
	3

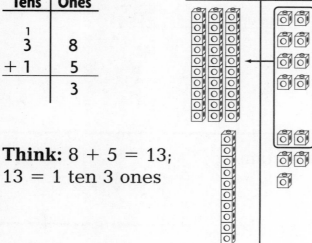

Step 2 Add the tens.

Tens	Ones
¹3	8
+ 1	5
5	3

Think: 8 + 5 = 13; 13 = 1 ten 3 ones

Think: 1 ten + 3 tens + 1 ten = 5 tens

So, 38 + 15 = 53

Find the sum. You may use connecting cubes.

1.
Tens	Ones
2	5
+ 3	7
6	2

2.
Tens	Ones
4	9
+ 2	1
7	0

3.
Tens	Ones
3	6
+ 2	6
6	2

4.
Tens	Ones
2	8
+ 2	6
5	4

5.
Tens	Ones
2	4
+ 3	5
5	9

6.
Tens	Ones
3	7
+ 5	8
9	5

7.
Tens	Ones
6	3
+ 1	8
8	1

8.
Tens	Ones
3	6
+ 2	9
6	5

Adding Two-Digit Numbers

You can regroup: 10 ones as 1 ten

10 tens as 1 hundred

Add 86 + 37.

Step 1 Add the ones.
If there are 10 or more, regroup
10 ones to make a ten.

Hundreds	Tens	Ones
	1	
	8	6
+	3	7
		3

Think: 6 + 7 = 13;
13 = 1 ten 3 ones

Step 2 Add the tens.
If there are 10 or more, regroup
10 tens to make a hundred.

Hundreds	Tens	Ones
	1	
	8	6
+	3	7
1	2	3

Think: 1 ten + 8 tens + 3 tens =
12 tens;
12 tens = 1 hundred 2 tens
So, 86 + 37 = 123.

Find the sum.

1.
H	T	O
	3	4
+	9	2
1	2	6

2.
H	T	O
	7	1
+	7	1
1	4	2

3.
H	T	O
	2	9
+	3	6
	6	5

4.
H	T	O
	9	0
+	8	5
1	7	5

5.
H	T	O
	2	7
+	9	7
1	2	4

6.
H	T	O
	3	6
+	7	9
1	1	5

7.
H	T	O
	5	8
+	5	8
1	1	6

8.
H	T	O
	7	2
+	5	8
1	3	0

Estimating Using a Number Line

You can use a number line to help round to the
nearest ten.

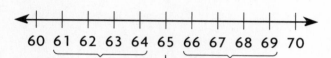

The numbers 61, 62,
63, and 64 are closer
to 60 than 70.
Round **down** to 60.

The numbers 66, 67,
68, and 69 are closer to
70 than 60.
Round **up** to 70.

65 is exactly
between 60 and 70.
Round 65 **up** to 70.

Round to the nearest ten. Use the number line.

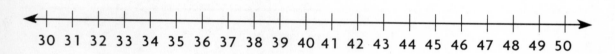

1. 34 → __30__

2. 39 → __40__

3. 42 → __40__

4. 47 → __50__

5. 35 → __40__

6. 33 → __30__

Ring the nearest ten.

7. 67 → 60 (70)

8. 43 → (40) 50

9. 26 → 20 (30)

10. 84 → (80) 90

11. 56 → 50 (60)

12. 18 → 10 (20)

**Estimate the sum by rounding. The first example is
completed for you.**

$$
\begin{array}{rr}
32 \to & 30 \\
+47 & +50 \\
\hline
& 80
\end{array}
$$

13.
$$
\begin{array}{rr}
42 \to & \underline{40} \\
+39 & +\ 40 \\
\hline
& 80
\end{array}
$$

14.
$$
\begin{array}{rr}
52 \to & \underline{50} \\
+21 & +\ 20 \\
\hline
& 70
\end{array}
$$

Choosing Addition or Subtraction

Kerry baked 9
gingerbread
cookies.

Scott baked 6
gingerbread
cookies.

How many cookies did Kerry and
Scott bake in all?

Add to find how many in all.
9 + 6 = 15

How many more cookies did
Kerry bake than Scott?

Subtract to compare the difference.
9 − 6 = 3

Write *add* or *subtract*. Then solve.

1. Kerry used 45 raisins to
   decorate her cookies. Scott
   used 25 raisins. How many
   raisins did they use in all?

   _____ **add; 70 raisins** _____

2. Kerry put nuts on 4 of her
   9 cookies. How many cookies
   do not have nuts?

   _____ **subtract; 5 cookies** _____

3. Kerry used 16 cinnamon
   candies. Scott used 9 cinnamon candies. How many
   more cinnamon candies did
   Kerry use than Scott?

   _____ **subtract; 7 more cinnamon** _____

   _____ **candies** _____

4. Kerry and Scott spent 12
   minutes washing the dishes
   and 6 minutes sweeping the
   floor. How much time did
   they spend cleaning up?

   _____ **add; 18 min** _____

5. Kerry is 12 years old. Scott is
   7 years old. How much older
   is Kerry than Scott?

   _____ **subtract; 5 years** _____

6. Kerry and Scott have
   15 cookies in all. If they give
   7 of the cookies away to
   friends, how many cookies
   will they have left?

   _____ **subtract; 8 cookies** _____

Problem-Solving Strategy

Write a Number Sentence

You can write a number sentence to solve a problem.
To write a number sentence, you need to ask yourself
the following two questions:

Which numbers should I use?
Read the problem. Look for numbers that might
be used to find the solution.

Should I add or subtract?

ADD
- to find the total
- to find how many in all

or

SUBTRACT
- to find how many are left
- to compare two amounts
- to find a missing part

Ring the numbers in each problem that will help you find
the solution. Complete the number sentence.
Put + or − in the ◯.

1. The pet store has ⟨19⟩ male gerbils and ⟨24⟩ female
   gerbils. How many gerbils are there in all?

   $\underset{\text{male gerbils}}{19} \; \oplus \; \underset{\text{female gerbils}}{24} \; = \; \underset{\text{total number of gerbils}}{43}$

2. The pet store has ⟨28⟩ goldfish. Mr. Fisk sells ⟨12⟩ of the
   goldfish. How many goldfish are left?

   $\underset{\text{number of goldfish}}{28} \; \ominus \; \underset{\text{goldfish sold}}{12} \; = \; \underset{\text{goldfish left}}{16}$

3. Mr. Fisk sells ⟨16⟩ rabbits and ⟨18⟩ guinea pigs in one
   month. How many more guinea pigs does he sell
   than rabbits?

   $\underset{\text{guinea pigs sold}}{18} \; \ominus \; \underset{\text{rabbits sold}}{16} \; = \; \underset{\substack{\text{difference between} \\ \text{guinea pigs sold and} \\ \text{rabbits sold}}}{2}$

Modeling Subtraction of Two-Digit Numbers

Sometimes you need to regroup when you subtract.

Subtract 51 − 26.

Step 1:

Decide whether to regroup.
Since 6 > 1, regroup.
5 tens 1 one = 4 tens 11 ones

Tens	Ones
⁴5̸	¹¹1̸
− 2	6

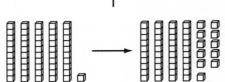

Step 2:

Subtract the ones.
11 − 6 = 5

Tens	Ones
⁴5̸	¹¹1̸
− 2	6
	5

Step 3:

Subtract the tens.
4 − 2 = 2

Tens	Ones
⁴5̸	¹¹1̸
− 2	6
2	5

Regroup. Find the difference. Use base-ten blocks.
In Exercises 1–2, the regrouping is done for you.

1.
Tens	Ones
²3̸	¹²2̸
− 1	6
1	6

2.
Tens	Ones
⁶7̸	¹¹1̸
− 5	4
1	7

3.
Tens	Ones
⁵6̸	¹⁵5̸
− 2	7
3	8

4.
Tens	Ones
⁶7̸	¹⁴4̸
− 4	9
2	5

5.
Tens	Ones
⁵6̸	¹⁷7̸
− 1	8
4	9

6.
Tens	Ones
¹2̸	¹⁴4̸
− 1	8
	6

7.
Tens	Ones
⁴5̸	¹³3̸
− 3	6
1	7

8.
Tens	Ones
³4̸	¹⁶6̸
− 2	9
1	7

Subtracting Two-Digit Numbers

In subtracting numbers, sometimes you need to regroup, and sometimes you do not.

Look at the numbers in the ones place.
Regroup if the number you are subtracting is **greater** than the number you are subtracting from.

Tens	Ones
6	3
− 1	2

2 < 3
No need to regroup.

Tens	Ones
$\overset{5}{\cancel{6}}$	$\overset{13}{\cancel{3}}$
− 4	9

9 > 3
Regroup.
6 tens 3 ones = 5 tens 13 ones

Regroup if necessary. Find the difference.

1.

Tens	Ones
5	2
− 2	1
3	1

2.

Tens	Ones
$\overset{4}{\cancel{5}}$	$\overset{12}{\cancel{2}}$
− 3	8
1	4

3.

Tens	Ones
7	5
− 3	4
4	1

4.

Tens	Ones
$\overset{6}{\cancel{7}}$	$\overset{15}{\cancel{5}}$
− 2	9
4	6

5.

Tens	Ones
$\overset{7}{\cancel{8}}$	$\overset{14}{\cancel{4}}$
− 4	7
3	7

6.

Tens	Ones
8	4
− 4	2
4	2

7.

Tens	Ones
4	7
− 2	6
2	1

8.

Tens	Ones
$\overset{3}{\cancel{4}}$	$\overset{17}{\cancel{7}}$
− 1	8
2	9

9.

Tens	Ones
6	8
− 3	5
3	3

10.

Tens	Ones
$\overset{3}{\cancel{4}}$	$\overset{12}{\cancel{2}}$
− 1	3
2	9

11.

Tens	Ones
$\overset{8}{\cancel{9}}$	$\overset{15}{\cancel{5}}$
− 6	7
2	8

12.

Tens	Ones
5	4
− 2	4
3	0

Subtracting with Zeros

Subtract 60 − 23.

Step 1:

Decide whether to regroup.
Since 3 > 0, regroup.
6 tens = 5 tens 10 ones

Tens	Ones
⁵6̸	¹⁰0̸
− 2	3

Step 2:

Subtract the ones.
10 − 3 = 7

Tens	Ones
⁵6̸	¹⁰0̸
− 2	3
	7

Step 3:

Subtract the tens.
5 − 2 = 3

Tens	Ones
⁵6̸	¹⁰0̸
− 2	3
3	7

Complete.

1. 3 tens = __2__ tens 10 ones   2. 7 tens = __6__ tens 10 ones

3. 9 tens = __8__ tens 10 ones   4. 5 tens = __4__ tens 10 ones

5. 8 tens = __7__ tens 10 ones   6. 4 tens = __3__ tens 10 ones

Regroup. Find the difference.

7.
$$
\begin{array}{r}
^{5}\,^{10} \\
6\!\!\!/\,0\!\!\!/ \\
-22 \\
\hline
38
\end{array}
$$

8.
$$
\begin{array}{r}
^{3}\,^{10} \\
4\!\!\!/\,0\!\!\!/ \\
-19 \\
\hline
21
\end{array}
$$

9.
$$
\begin{array}{r}
^{6}\,^{10} \\
7\!\!\!/\,0\!\!\!/ \\
-28 \\
\hline
42
\end{array}
$$

10.
$$
\begin{array}{r}
^{2}\,^{10} \\
3\!\!\!/\,0\!\!\!/ \\
-15 \\
\hline
15
\end{array}
$$

11.
$$
\begin{array}{r}
^{1}\,^{10} \\
2\!\!\!/\,0\!\!\!/ \\
-\ \ 6 \\
\hline
14
\end{array}
$$

12.
$$
\begin{array}{r}
^{4}\,^{10} \\
5\!\!\!/\,0\!\!\!/ \\
-37 \\
\hline
13
\end{array}
$$

13.
$$
\begin{array}{r}
^{7}\,^{10} \\
8\!\!\!/\,0\!\!\!/ \\
-53 \\
\hline
27
\end{array}
$$

14.
$$
\begin{array}{r}
^{8}\,^{10} \\
9\!\!\!/\,0\!\!\!/ \\
-36 \\
\hline
54
\end{array}
$$

Practicing Subtraction

Subtraction can be used to answer different kinds
of questions.

How many more black marbles
than white marbles are there?

John has 8 stickers. He gives
3 of them away. How many
stickers does John have left?

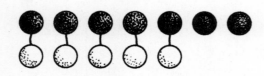

Subtract to find *how many more*
or *how many fewer.*
7 − 5 = 2

Subtract to find *how many
are left.*
8 − 3 = 5

Solve. Show your work next to each problem.

1. Tanya collects 32 shells,
and Joan collects 25
shells. How many
more shells does Tanya
collect than Joan?

$$\begin{array}{r} 32 \\ -25 \\ \hline 7 \end{array}$$

_____**7 more shells**_____

2. Tanya gives 16 of her
32 shells to her brother.
How many shells does
Tanya have left?

$$\begin{array}{r} 32 \\ -16 \\ \hline 16 \end{array}$$

_____**16 shells**_____

3. Toby is 56 inches tall,
and Sam is 48 inches
tall. How much taller
is Toby than Sam?

$$\begin{array}{r} 56 \\ -48 \\ \hline 8 \end{array}$$

_____**8 in. taller**_____

4. Anne picks 42 straw-
berries. She eats 17 of
them. How many
strawberries are left?

$$\begin{array}{r} 42 \\ -17 \\ \hline 25 \end{array}$$

_____**25 strawberries**_____

5. Roberto has 75¢. He
buys a ball for 39¢.
How much money
does Roberto have
left?

$$\begin{array}{r} 75¢ \\ -39¢ \\ \hline 36¢ \end{array}$$

_____**36¢ left**_____

6. Julio and Jan count
their pennies. Julio
has 48¢, and Jan has
72¢. How much more
money does Jan have?

$$\begin{array}{r} 72¢ \\ -48¢ \\ \hline 24¢ \end{array}$$

_____**24¢ more**_____

Harcourt Brace School Publishers

Using Addition and Subtraction

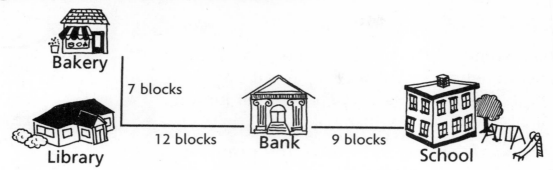

Bakery

7 blocks

12 blocks   Bank   9 blocks

Library   School

Phil rides his bike from school to the library. How many blocks does he ride?

You can *add* to find the total number of blocks.

$$\begin{array}{r} 9 \text{ blocks from school to bank} \\ +12 \text{ blocks from bank to library} \\ \hline 21 \end{array}$$

So, Phil rides 21 blocks.

How much closer is the library to the bakery than to the bank?

You can *subtract* to compare the number of blocks.

$$\begin{array}{r} 12 \text{ blocks from library to bank} \\ - 7 \text{ blocks from library to bakery} \\ \hline 5 \end{array}$$

So, the library is 5 blocks closer to the bakery than to the bank.

For Problems 1–5, use the map.

1. Mr. Turner drives from Adams to Lincoln. How many miles does he drive?

<u>**55 mi**</u>

Adams

37 mi   18 mi   26 mi   Jefferson

Wilson   Lincoln

2. Sam lives in Wilson. Would it be farther for him to drive to Adams or to Jefferson?

<u>**Jefferson**</u>

3. Jerry lives in Lincoln. How much closer does he live to Wilson than to Jefferson?

<u>**8 mi closer**</u>

4. Jerry's mother drives from Lincoln to Jefferson and back to Lincoln. How many miles does she drive?

<u>**52 mi**</u>

5. Mr. Bishop is driving from Adams to Wilson. After driving 15 miles, he stops to get gas. How much farther does he have to drive to get to Wilson?

<u>**22 mi**</u>

Problem-Solving Strategy

Work Backward

Lisa had some money in her wallet. On the way to the store, she found 10¢. She spent 25¢ for a gum ball. She now has 53¢. How much money did Lisa have to start with?

Start

You can *work backward* to solve the problem.

Start → 53¢   Begin with the money Lisa has now.

53¢ + 25¢ = 78¢   Add the money Lisa spent.

78¢ − 10¢ = 68¢   Subtract the money Lisa found.

So, Lisa had 68¢ in her wallet to start with.

Found 10¢
Spent 25¢

Work backward to solve.

1. Mrs. Green baked some pies in the morning. In the afternoon, she baked 7 more pies. During the day, she sold 12 pies. She now has 4 pies left. How many pies did Mrs. Green bake in the morning?

_____4_____ number of pies left

_4 + 12 = 16_ Add the number of pies sold.

_16 − 7 = 9_ Subtract number of pies baked in the afternoon.

_____9_____ number of pies Mrs. Green baked in the morning

2. Lily borrowed a large stack of library books last week. This week she returned 14 books and checked out 2 new books. She now has 9 library books. How many books did Lily borrow last week?

_____ **21 books** _____

3. Carlos counted his toy cars before his birthday. On his birthday, he got 3 new cars. The next day, Carlos gave 5 of his old cars to his younger brother. He now has 12 cars. How many cars did Carlos have before his birthday?

_____ **14 cars** _____

Adding Three-Digit Numbers

You can regroup: 10 ones as 1 ten

10 tens as 1 hundred

Add 248 + 395.

Step 1

Add the ones.
8 + 5 = 13 ones
13 ones =
1 ten 3 ones

Hundreds	Tens	Ones
	1	
2	4	8
+ 3	9	5
		3

Step 2

Add the tens.
1 + 4 + 9 = 14 tens
14 tens =
1 hundred 4 tens

Hundreds	Tens	Ones
1	1	
2	4	8
+ 3	9	5
	4	3

Step 3

Add the hundreds.
1 + 2 + 3 = 6 hundreds

Hundreds	Tens	Ones
1	1	
2	4	8
+ 3	9	5
6	4	3

Find the sum.

1.
H	T	O
3	5	6
+1	2	8
4	8	4

2.
H	T	O
3	5	6
+4	9	1
8	4	7

3.
H	T	O
2	4	6
+6	7	8
9	2	4

4.
H	T	O
4	5	9
+3	5	3
8	1	2

5.
H	T	O
4	0	9
+4	5	9
8	6	8

6.
H	T	O
6	3	1
+2	8	7
9	1	8

7.
H	T	O
1	9	4
+1	8	9
3	8	3

8.
H	T	O
7	6	5
+1	6	5
9	3	0

Adding More Than Two Addends

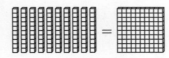 = |

10 ones = 1 ten

|||||||||| = ▦

10 tens = 1 hundred

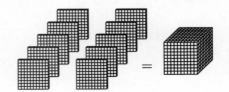 = ◼

10 hundreds =
1 thousand

Add 645 + 364 + 832.

Step 1

Add the ones.
5 + 4 + 2 = 11 ones
11 ones = 1 ten 1 one

Step 2

Add the tens.
1 + 4 + 6 + 3 = 14 tens
14 tens =
1 hundred 4 tens

Step 3

Add the hundreds.
1 + 6 + 3 + 8 =
18 hundreds
18 hundreds =
1 thousand
8 hundreds

Thousands	Hundreds	Tens	Ones
			1
	6	4	5
	3	6	4
+	8	3	2
			1

Thousands	Hundreds	Tens	Ones
		1	1
	6	4	5
	3	6	4
+	8	3	2
		4	1

Thousands	Hundreds	Tens	Ones
1		1	1
	6	4	5
	3	6	4
+	8	3	2
1,		8	4	1

Find the sum.

1.

Th	H	T	O
	3	4	1
	5	6	2
+	5	3	4
1,	4	3	7

2.

Th	H	T	O
	3	2	9
	7	1	1
+	5	3	6
1,	5	7	6

3.

Th	H	T	O
	6	7	5
	3	2	5
+	1	4	2
1,	1	4	2

4.

Th	H	T	O
	2	8	4
	7	2	9
+	5	6	3
1,	5	7	6

Subtracting Three-Digit Numbers

Sometimes you need to regroup more than once in a
subtraction problem.

Subtract 546 − 379.

Step 1	**Step 2**	**Step 3**
Look at the ones. 9 > 6 Regroup. 4 tens 6 ones = 3 tens 16 ones	Look at the tens. 7 > 3 Regroup. 5 hundreds 3 tens = 4 hundreds 13 tens	
Subtract the ones. 16 − 9 = 7 ones	Subtract the tens. 13 − 7 = 6 tens	Subtract the hundreds. 4 − 3 = 1 hundred

Step 1

Hundreds	Tens	Ones
5	³4̸	¹⁶6̸
− 3	7	9
		7

Step 2

Hundreds	Tens	Ones
⁴5̸	¹³4̸	¹⁶6̸
− 3	7	9
	6	7

Step 3

Hundreds	Tens	Ones
⁴5̸	¹³4̸	¹⁶6̸
− 3	7	9
1	6	7

Find the difference.

1.

H	T	O
8	2	9
−6	8	1
1	4	8

2.

H	T	O
4	3	5
−1	2	9
3	0	6

3.

H	T	O
5	2	4
−2	8	9
2	3	5

4.

H	T	O
8	2	5
−1	5	6
6	6	9

5.

H	T	O
3	5	6
−1	9	2
1	6	4

6.

H	T	O
4	3	5
−1	3	8
2	9	7

7.

H	T	O
3	9	4
−2	7	5
1	1	9

8.

H	T	O
7	7	6
−5	8	9
1	8	7

Problem-Solving Strategy

Guess and Check

Sometimes you can find an answer by first guessing and then checking your answer.

Mary has 20 red and blue balloons at her party. She has 4 more red balloons than blue balloons. How many balloons of each color does she have?

	Blue	Red	Total	Notes
Guess 1	5	$5 + 4 = 9$	$5 + 9 = 14$	too low
Guess 2	10	$10 + 4 = 14$	$10 + 14 = 24$	too high
Guess 3	8	$8 + 4 = 12$	$8 + 12 = 20$	just right

Mary has 8 blue balloons and 12 red balloons.

Use *guess and check* to solve. You may wish to make your own tables.

1. Peter delivers 110 newspapers on the weekend. He delivers 20 more newspapers on Sunday than on Saturday. How many newspapers does he deliver each day?

   <u>**45 newspapers on Saturday;**</u>

   <u>**65 newspapers on Sunday**</u>

2. Paul is 5 years older than Lisa. The sum of their ages is 19. How old is each person?

   <u>**Lisa is 7; Paul is 12.**</u>

3. Jesse has earned $40 more by washing cars than Tyrone has by raking leaves. Together they have $140. How much has each boy earned?

   <u>**Jesse has earned $90;**</u>

   <u>**Tyrone has earned $50.**</u>

Harcourt Brace School Publishers

Subtracting Across Zeros

300
−126
?

How can you subtract 126 from 300?
You can't subtract from 0 ones or
0 tens, so regroup the hundreds.

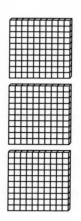

3 hundreds

=

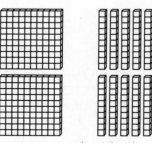

Regroup 3 hundreds
as
2 hundreds 10 tens

=

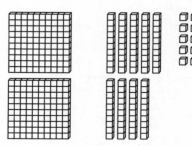

Regroup 2 hundreds 10 tens
as
2 hundreds 9 tens 10 ones

300
−126

2 10
3̸0̸0
−126

9
2 10 10
3̸0̸0̸
−126
174

Complete.

1. 5 hundreds = 4 hundreds __10__ tens

5 hundreds = 4 hundreds 9 tens __10__ ones

2. 7 hundreds = __6__ hundreds 10 tens

7 hundreds = 6 hundreds __9__ tens 10 ones

Show how you would regroup before subtracting.

3.

H	T	O
5̸ 6	9 10 0̸	10 0̸
− 2	5	7
3	4	3

4.

H	T	O
4̸ 5	9 10 0̸	10 0̸
− 1	5	1
3	4	9

5.

H	T	O
7̸ 8	9 10 0̸	10 0̸
− 4	3	7
3	6	3

6.

H	T	O
2̸ 3	9 10 0̸	10 0̸
− 1	6	2
1	3	8

More About Subtracting Across Zeros

Subtract 605 − 238.

Step 1

Regroup.
6 hundreds 0 tens =
5 hundreds 10 tens

Hundreds	Tens	Ones
⁵6̸	¹⁰0̸	5
− 2	3	8

Step 2

Regroup.
10 tens 5 ones =
9 tens 15 ones

Hundreds	Tens	Ones
⁵6̸	⁹¹⁰0̸	¹⁵5̸
− 2	3	8

Step 3

Regroup.
a. Subtract the ones.
b. Subtract the tens.
c. Subtract the hundreds.

Hundreds	Tens	Ones
⁵6̸	⁹¹⁰0̸	¹⁵5̸
− 2	3	8
3	6	7

Complete.

1. 8 hundreds 0 tens 4 ones =

   7 hundreds __10__ tens 4 ones =

   7 hundreds 9 tens __14__ ones

2. 4 hundreds 0 tens 6 ones =

   __3__ hundreds 10 tens 6 ones =

   3 hundreds __9__ tens 16 ones

Find the difference.

3.
H	T	O
3	0	6
−1	4	9
1	5	7

4.
H	T	O
4	0	1
−2	9	8
1	0	3

5.
H	T	O
6	0	7
−1	2	8
4	7	9

6.
H	T	O
9	0	1
−2	5	5
6	4	6

7.
H	T	O
4	0	0
−1	2	5
2	7	5

8.
H	T	O
6	0	0
−4	2	5
1	7	5

9.
H	T	O
7	0	0
−1	0	8
5	9	2

10.
H	T	O
5	0	0
−4	3	2
	6	8

Understanding a Clock

The **hour hand** is the short hand on a clock. Use it to tell the hour.

The **minute hand** is the long hand on a clock. Use it to tell the number of minutes.

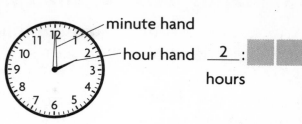

minute hand
hour hand
__2__ : ▢ ▢
hours

It takes the minute hand 5 minutes to move from one number to the next. So, you can skip count by fives to find the number of minutes.

5 minutes

▢ : 1 5
minutes

▢ : 3 0
minutes

▢ : 4 5
minutes

▢ : 0 0 ○ ◯
minutes

When the minute hand is on the 12, write 00 for the minutes.

Write the number of hours.

1.

__7__ : ▢ ▢
hours

2.

__12__ : ▢ ▢
hours

3.

__3__ : ▢ ▢
hours

4.

__8__ : ▢ ▢
hours

Skip count by fives. Write the number of minutes.

5.

▢ : 2 5
minutes

6.

▢ : 1 0
minutes

7.

▢ : 0 0
minutes

8.

▢ : 3 5
minutes

Estimating Minutes and Hours

A **minute** is a short amount of time. In about one minute you can

- brush your teeth.
- say the alphabet.
- drink a glass of juice.

An **hour** is a longer amount of time. An hour is 60 minutes. In about one hour you can
- read a story.
- take a walk.
- paint a picture.

Write *hours* or *minutes* to tell how you would measure the time for each activity.

1. read a long book

_____ **hr** _____

2. jump rope at recess

_____ **min** _____

3. put away the groceries

_____ **min** _____

4. build a doghouse

_____ **hr** _____

5. watch a baseball game

_____ **hr** _____

6. set the table

_____ **min** _____

Circle the better estimate.

7. feed the cat   (2 minutes) or 2 hours

8. watch a movie   2 minutes or (2 hours)

9. knit a mitten   4 minutes or (4 hours)

Decide if the estimated time makes sense. Write *yes* or *no*.

10. It takes about 2 minutes to drive to another city. _____ **no** _____

11. It takes about 5 hours to make a sandwich. _____ **no** _____

12. It takes about 2 hours to visit a museum. _____ **yes** _____

13. It takes about 30 minutes to write a letter. _____ **yes** _____

14. It takes about 1 hour to ring a doorbell. _____ **no** _____

15. It takes about 10 hours to eat a banana. _____ **no** _____

Harcourt Brace School Publishers

Time to the Minute

How many minutes after 10:00 is it?

10: _?_ _?_

To count the number of minutes
after the hour, follow these steps:

Start at 12. Count by
fives as far as you can.

5 minutes
10 minutes
15 minutes
20 minutes
25 minutes
30 minutes
35 minutes
40 minutes

Then count by ones to where the
minute hand is pointing. Add.

40 + 2 = 42

So, it is 42 minutes after 10, or 10:42.

Show how you add to find the number of minutes. Write
the time.

1.

__15__ + __3__ = __18__

10:__18__

2.

__30__ + __4__ = __34__

10:__34__

3.

__55__ + __2__ = __57__

10:__57__

4.

__20__ + __1__ = __21__

10:__21__

Time After the Hour

You can read the time shown on a clock in different ways.

- One way is to read the hour first and then the minutes.

- Another way is to read the minutes first and then the hour. Include the words *minutes after*.

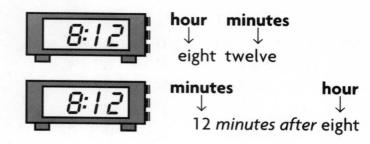

Draw a line to match the clock and a way to read the time.

1. 36 minutes after four

2. seven eighteen

3. 23 minutes after eleven

4. two fifty-seven

5. 44 minutes after twelve

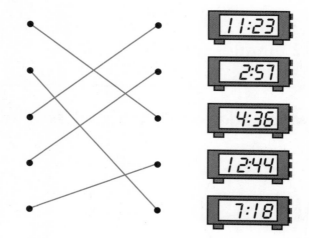

Circle the minutes. Write each time with the minutes first. The first one is done for you.

6. 3:(51)

   __51__ min after __3__

7. 10:(18)

   __18__ min after __10__

8. 5:(42)

   __42__ min after __5__

9. 9:(39)

   __39__ min after __9__

10. 1:27

   __27__ min after __1__

11. 6:53

   __53__ min after __6__

Problem-Solving Strategy

Act It Out

Leroy went to the park. He got there at 24 minutes after two. Where were the hands on the clock when Leroy got to the park?

Use a clock with hour and minute hands to **act the problem out.**

5 minutes
10 minutes
15 minutes
20 minutes
24 minutes

To know where to point the hour hand, look at the number of minutes.

If the number of minutes

equals 30, point the hour hand exactly between the 2 and 3.

is **less than 30,** point the hour hand closer to the 2.

is **greater than 30,** point the hour hand closer to the 3.

The number of minutes is 24. That is less than 30, so point the hour hand closer to the 2.

24 minutes after 2

Use a clock. Tell where the hour hand is pointing.

1. 38 minutes after 4   between __4__ and __5__, but closer to __5__

2. 56 minutes after 9   between __9__ and __10__, but closer to __10__

3. 16 minutes after 12   between __12__ and __1__, but closer to __12__

4. 7 minutes after 1   between __1__ and __2__, but closer to __1__

Elapsed Time: Minutes and Hours

Elapsed time is the time that passes from the start of an activity to the end of that activity. To find the elapsed time, count the number of minutes between the start time and the end time.

Start: End: Elapsed time:

30 minutes

6:15   6:45

Remember:
- The minute hand moves one number every 5 minutes.
- The minute hand moves three numbers every 15 minutes.

Draw the minute hand to show the start time and the end time. Then find the elapsed time.

	Start	End	Elapsed Time
1.	1:30	1:45	15 min
2.	6:45	7:30	45 min
3.	10:00	11:15	1 hr 15 min
4.	5:30	6:00	30 min

Name _____

Using Time Schedules

A **schedule** is a table that lists activities and the times they happen.

John is interested in animal training. He wants to know how long the animal trainer will be performing.

PERFORMANCE SCHEDULE		
Performer	**Time**	**Room**
Juggler	1:00–1:45	1
Animal trainer	2:15–3:00	1
Clown	1:15–2:15	2
Folk singer	2:30–4:00	2
Storyteller	2:30–3:45	3

• Find *Animal trainer* in the column of performers.

• Read across to find the time of the performance.

• Find the elapsed time from 2:15 to 3:00.

The animal trainer will be performing for 45 minutes.

For Problems 1–6, use the schedule.

1. In which room will the animal trainer perform?

    Room 1

2. For how long will the juggler perform?

    45 min

3. Who will perform in Room 2?

    clown;

    folk singer

4. Which performer will perform for 1 hour and 15 minutes?

    storyteller

5. Rosa plans to watch the clown and the animal trainer. How much time will she spend watching performances?

    1 hr 45 min

6. Which performer has the longest show?

    folk singer

Scheduling Time: Minutes and Hours

Carrie made a plan for how she would spend her time after school.

Carrie started to make a schedule for her activities. She gets home from school at 3:00.

Each activity begins when the activity before it ends.

Activity	Elapsed Time
Snack	15 minutes
Walk dog	15 minutes
Homework	45 minutes
Play outside	1 hour
Read	30 minutes
Chores	15 minutes

1. Use the information from Carrie's plan to complete her schedule. The first two activities are completed for you.

Activity	Start Time	End Time	Elapsed Time
Snack	3:00	3:15	15 minutes
Walk dog	3:15	3:30	15 minutes
Homework	3:30	4:15	45 min
Play outside	4:15	5:15	1 hr
Read	5:15	5:45	30 min
Chores	5:45	6:00	15 min

2. Make up a schedule that shows three activities you plan to do after school. **Check students' schedules.**

Activity	Start Time	End Time	Elapsed Time

Harcourt Brace School Publishers

Scheduling Time: Days and Weeks

Lisa would like to take a class at the Arts Center Summer Camp. She will be on vacation during Week 1. She plans to take swimming lessons from 2:00 to 3:00 every day during Weeks 2, 3, and 4.

Which classes can Lisa choose from?

ARTS CENTER SUMMER CAMP SCHEDULE		
Class	Week	Time
Art for Horse Lovers	1	9:00–12:00
Art for Cat Lovers	2	9:00–12:00
Bookmaking	2	1:00–4:00
Theater	3	9:00–12:00
Jewelry	4	1:00–4:00
Pottery	4	1:00–4:00

- Lisa **cannot** take *Art for Horse Lovers* because it meets during Week 1.

- Lisa **cannot** take *Bookmaking*, *Jewelry*, or *Pottery* because they meet during the afternoon.

- Lisa **can** choose either *Art for Cat Lovers* or *Theatre*.

For Problems 1–4, use the schedule.

1. Gina is interested in both *Jewelry* and *Pottery*. Can she take both classes? Explain.

   Possible answer:

   No. The classes meet

   at the same time.

2. Would it be possible for Jeff to take *Art for Cat Lovers* and *Theater?* Explain your answer.

   Possible answer:

   Yes. The classes meet

   during different weeks.

3. Paco plans to take *Art for Cat Lovers* and *Bookmaking*. He will eat his lunch at the Arts Center. How many hours will he spend at the Arts Center each day?

   7 hr

4. Kito can walk to the Arts Center in 15 minutes. If he takes *Bookmaking*, what time will he need to leave his house in order to get to class on time?

   12:45

Elapsed Time: Days, Weeks, and Months

Jack's cat had 4 kittens on May 15. It is now June 5. How many days old are the kittens?

Start at May 15 and count on until you reach June 5. Do **not** count the day you start on.

The kittens are 21 days old.

May						
Sun	Mon	Tue	Wed	Thu	Fri	Sat
	1	2	3	4	5	6
7	8	9	10	11	12	13
14	(15)	16	17	18	19	20
21	22	23	24	25	26	27
28	29	30	31			

How many weeks old are the kittens?

Start at May 15 and count weeks by moving down on the calendars until you reach June 5.

The kittens are 3 weeks old.

June						
Sun	Mon	Tue	Wed	Thu	Fri	Sat
				1	2	3
4	(5)	6	7	8	9	10
11	12	13	14	15	16	17
18	19	20	21	22	23	24
25	26	27	28	29	30	

For Problems 1–4, use the calendars.

1. The kittens first opened their eyes when they were 7 days old. On what date did they first open their eyes?

    May 22

2. Jack read a book about kittens every day from May 17 to May 22. How many days did Jack read about kittens?

    5 days

3. Jack read that kittens are usually able to walk when they are 4 weeks old. On what date will Jack's kittens be 4 weeks old?

    June 12

4. Jack needs to take his kittens to the veterinarian on June 26. How many weeks old will the kittens be on June 26?

    6 wk old

Harcourt Brace School Publishers

Problem-Solving Strategy

Work Backward

Tyler and Melissa are putting on a puppet show this afternoon. It is now 10:00. They just spent 30 minutes practicing for their show. Before that, they spent 15 minutes setting up the puppet theater. At what time did they start setting up the theater?

You can **work backward** to solve this problem.

Time now: Time Tyler and Melissa   Time Tyler and Melissa
              started practicing: started setting up the theater:

10:00

9:30

9:15

Tyler and Melissa started setting up the theater at 9:15.

Work backward to solve. You may use a clock with hands that move.

1. It is now 12:45. Tyler and Melissa just spent 30 minutes eating lunch. Before that, they spent 1 hour riding their bikes. At what time did they start riding bikes?

    11:15

2. It is now 3:30. Tina just spent 15 minutes walking home. Before that, she spent 45 minutes watching the puppet show. At what time did the puppet show begin?

    2:30

3. It is now 2:00. Melissa just spent 30 minutes making lemonade and popcorn for the puppet show. Before that, she spent 15 minutes setting up chairs. At what time did she begin setting up chairs?

    1:15

4. It is now 4:15. Tyler and Melissa just spent 15 minutes reading. Before that, they spent 30 minutes cleaning up after the puppet show. At what time did they begin cleaning up?

    3:30

Name _____

Counting Bills and Coins

You can count sets of bills and coins by following these steps:

Step 1 Count the bills first, from greatest to least value.

Step 2 Count the coins, from greatest to least value.

Step 3 Write the total, using the dollar sign and the decimal point.

Count this group of bills and coins.

Count: $5.00 $6.00 $6.25 $6.50 $6.55 $6.56 $6.57

Write: $6.57   **Read:** six dollars and fifty-seven cents

$6.57

6 dollars ——————— 57 cents

decimal point

- The number before the decimal point shows the number of dollars.

- The number after the decimal point shows the number of cents.

Count each group of bills and coins. Write each new amount as you count, using the dollar sign and decimal point.

1.

   $5.00 $5.10 $5.15 $5.20 $5.21

2.

   $1.00 $2.00 $2.25 $2.50 $2.60 $2.65

3.

   $5.00 $6.00 $6.25 $6.35 $6.45 $6.50 $6.51

Making Equivalent Sets

Sets that are **equivalent** name the same amount.

The two sets of coins shown below are equivalent. Each
set of coins has a value of $0.50.

Count: $0.25 $0.50	**Count:** $0.10 $0.20 $0.30 $0.40 $0.45 $0.50

Write the value of each set of coins, using the dollar
sign and the decimal point. Then draw a picture of an
equivalent set. **Check students' drawings. Possible answers are given.**

1.

_____ $0.26

2.

_____ $0.35

3.

_____ $0.80

4.

_____ $0.32

Name _____

Comparing Amounts

You can compare amounts of money by following these steps:

Step 1 Count each group of bills and coins.

Step 2 Write the total value of each group, using the
dollar sign and the decimal point.

Step 3 Compare the totals. Which amount is greater?

$1.00 $1.25 $1.35 $1.00 $1.10 $1.20 $1.25 $1.26
Total: $1.35   **Total:** $1.26

$1.35 is greater than $1.26.

Write the total value of each group of bills and coins,
using the dollar sign and the decimal point. Then circle
the letter of the greater amount.

1. **a.**   **b.**

Total: _____ **$2.75** _____   Total: _____ **$2.65** _____

2. **a.**    **b.**

Total: _____ **$2.11** _____   Total: _____ **$2.10** _____

3. **a.**   **b.**

Total: _____ **$5.41** _____   Total: _____ **$5.50** _____

Making Change

Mr. Cook sells a muffin that cost $0.69. Mrs. Lopez gives Mr. Cook a $1 bill. Mr. Cook counts out the change. He starts with the price of the muffin and begins counting on with coins that have the least value to make $1.00.

 $0.69 + + + =

$0.69 $0.70 $0.75 $1.00

money given $1.00   change given $0.31

Complete the table. Count the change. Draw the coin or bill that is missing in each set of change.

	Money Given	Item Sold	Change Given			
1.	$1.00	$0.35	$0.40	$0.50	$0.75	$1.00
2.	$1.00	$0.92	$0.93	$0.94	$0.95	$1.00
3.	$1.00	$0.79	$0.80	$0.90	$1.00	
4.	$5.00	$3.74	$3.75	$4.00	$5.00	

Adding and Subtracting Money

Adding money is similar to adding whole numbers.
Add $2.75 + $3.97.

Step 1
Add pennies.

Dollars	Dimes	Pennies
	1	
$2.	7	5
+ 3.	9	7
		2

Step 2
Add dimes.

Dollars	Dimes	Pennies
1	1	
$2.	7	5
+ 3.	9	7
	7	2

Step 3
Add dollars.

Dollars	Dimes	Pennies
1	1	
$2.	7	5
+ 3.	9	7
$6.	7	2

The dollar sign is placed in front of the first number in the sum.

The decimal point separates dollars from cents.

Subtracting money is similar to subtracting whole numbers.

Find the sum. Remember to place the dollar sign and decimal point in your answer.

1.

Dollars	Dimes	Pennies
$4.	3	9
+ 2.	8	5
$7.	2	4

2.

Dollars	Dimes	Pennies
$5.	3	9
+ 2.	0	9
$7.	4	8

3.

Dollars	Dimes	Pennies
$ 9.	4	2
+ 1.	3	9
$10.	8	1

Find the difference.

4.

Dollars	Dimes	Pennies
$4.	3	5
− 1.	2	9
$3.	0	6

5.

Dollars	Dimes	Pennies
$4.	2	5
− 2.	8	0
$1.	4	5

6.

Dollars	Dimes	Pennies
$4.	3	0
− 1.	8	5
$2.	4	5

Harcourt Brace School Publishers

Problem-Solving Strategy

Write a Number Sentence

You can write a number sentence to solve a problem about money. To write a number sentence, you need to ask yourself the following two questions:

Which numbers should I use?
Read the problem. Look for numbers that might be used to find the solution.

Which operation should I use?

ADD

• to find the total amount.

SUBTRACT

• to find how much is left.
• to find the change.
• to compare two amounts.

Example: Tim buys a set of paints for $4.39 and a paint brush for $0.79. How much does Tim spend in all?

Write: $4.39 + $0.79 = ?
$$\begin{array}{r} \$4.39 \\ + 0.79 \\ \hline \$5.18 \end{array}$$
So, Tim will spend $5.18.

Write a number sentence to solve. Then add or subtract to find the solution. Put + or − in the ◯ .

1. Mary buys a hat for $3.49. She gives the clerk $5.00. How much change will Mary get?

$5.00 ⊖ $3.49 = $1.51

$$\begin{array}{r} \$5.00 \\ - 3.49 \\ \hline \$1.51 \end{array}$$

2. Alice had $5.50 in her wallet. She buys a scarf that costs $2.85. How much money does Alice have left?

$5.50 ⊖ $2.85 = $2.65

$$\begin{array}{r} \$5.50 \\ - 2.85 \\ \hline \$2.65 \end{array}$$

Name _____

Ways to Use Numbers

This calendar shows January, February, March, and April.

January

Sun	Mon	Tue	Wed	Thu	Fri	Sat
		1	2	3	4	5
6	7	8	9	10	11	12
13	14	15	16	17	18	19
20	21	22	23	24	25	26
27	28	29	30	31		

February

Sun	Mon	Tue	Wed	Thu	Fri	Sat
					1	2
3	4	5	6	7	8	9
10	11	12	13	14	15	16
17	18	19	20	21	22	23
24	25	26	27	28		

March

Sun	Mon	Tue	Wed	Thu	Fri	Sat
					1	2
3	4	5	6	7	8	9
10	11	12	13	14	15	16
17	18	19	20	21	22	23
24	25	26	27	28	29	30
31						

April

Sun	Mon	Tue	Wed	Thu	Fri	Sat
	1	2	3	4	5	6
7	8	9	10	11	12	13
14	15	16	17	18	19	20
21	22	23	24	25	26	27
28	29	30				

Cardinal numbers tell how many.
Example: There are **12** months in the year.

Ordinal numbers show position or order.
Example: January is the **first** month of the year.

For Exercises 1–3, use a cardinal number in your answer.

1. How many days are there in March?

   31 days

2. How many Mondays are there in April?

   5 Mondays

3. How many days are there in February?

   28 days

4. Which month has exactly 30 days?

   April

Write the name of the month for each ordinal number.

5. second _____**February**_____

6. fourth _____**April**_____

Understanding 100's

Hundreds	Tens	Ones
1 hundred = 10 tens 1 hundred = 100 ones	1 ten = 10 ones	1 one

Complete.

1. ___10___ tens = 1 hundred   2. ___10___ ones = 1 ten

3. ___100___ ones = 1 hundred   4. ___10___ tens = 100 ones

5. 10 ___tens___ = 1 hundred   6. 10 ___ones___ = 1 ten

7. 1 ___hundred___ = 10 tens   8. 1 ___ten___ = 10 ones

Dollars	Dimes	Pennies
1 dollar = 10 dimes 1 dollar = 100 pennies	1 dime = 10 pennies	1 penny

Complete.

9. ___100___ pennies = 1 dollar   10. ___10___ pennies = 1 dime

11. ___10___ dimes = 1 dollar   12. ___100___ pennies = 10 dimes

13. 1 ___dollar___ = 10 dimes   14. 1 ___dime___ = 10 pennies

15. 1 ___dollar___ = 100 pennies   16. 100 pennies = 10 ___dimes___

Number Patterns

Numbers can be arranged in dot patterns.

Even numbers have pairs of dots.

Odd numbers have pairs of dots, with one dot left over.

Write the number of dots in each set.
Circle the even numbers.

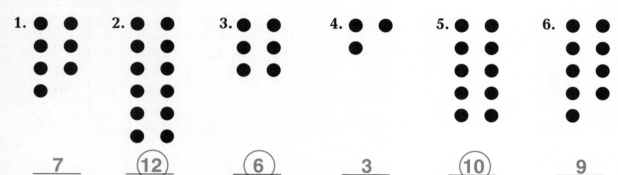

1. _7_   2. (12)   3. (6)   4. _3_   5. (10)   6. _9_

Even numbers end with 0, 2, 4, 6, and 8.

7. Circle the even numbers in the chart below.

1	(2)	3	(4)	5	(6)	7	(8)	9	(10)
11	(12)	13	(14)	15	(16)	17	(18)	19	(20)
21	(22)	23	(24)	25	(26)	27	(28)	29	(30)
31	(32)	33	(34)	35	(36)	37	(38)	39	(40)

Numbers that are not even are odd.

8. Odd numbers end with _1_, _3_, _5_, _7_, and _9_.

Patterns of Tens

You can use the hundred chart to add and subtract tens.

What is 25 + 10?

- Find 25 on the hundred chart.
- Move **down** one square.
25 + 10 = 35

What is 49 − 10?

- Find 49.
- Move **up** one square.
49 − 10 = 39

When you add or subtract 10, the digit in the ones place does **not** change.
Example: 3**6** + 10 = 4**6**
64 − 10 = 54

1	2	3	4	5	6	7	8	9	10
11	12	13	14	15	16	17	18	19	20
21	22	23	24	25	26	27	28	29	30
31	32	33	34	35	36	37	38	39	40
41	42	43	44	45	46	47	48	49	50
51	52	53	54	55	56	57	58	59	60
61	62	63	64	65	66	67	68	69	70
71	72	73	74	75	76	77	78	79	80
81	82	83	84	85	86	87	88	89	90
91	92	93	94	95	96	97	98	99	100

Find the sum or difference. You may use the hundred chart.

1. 39 + 10 = __49__
2. 86 − 10 = __76__
3. 17 + 10 = __27__
4. 24 + 10 = __34__
5. 87 + 10 = __97__
6. 95 − 10 = __85__
7. 52 + 10 = __62__
8. 60 − 10 = __50__
9. 43 − 10 = __33__

10. What is 26 + 30?
- Find 26.
- Move down 3 squares.

26 + 30 = __56__

11. What is 41 + 50?
- Find 41.
- Move down 5 squares.

41 + 50 = __91__

12. What is 78 − 20?
- Find 78.
- Move up 2 squares.

78 − 20 = __58__

13. What is 67 − 40?
- Find 67.
- Move up 4 squares.

67 − 40 = __27__

Using Benchmark Numbers

Benchmark numbers are useful numbers like 10, 25, 50, and 100 that help you see their relationship to other numbers.

You can use benchmark numbers to estimate the number of tiles on a floor.

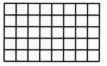

Choose a benchmark number, such as 10, and count that number of tiles.

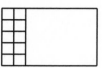

Estimate that there are about 4 groups of 10 tiles on the whole floor.
10 + 10 + 10 + 10 = 40

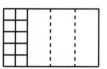

Estimate the number of tiles on each floor. Use the tiles that are shown as benchmarks.

1.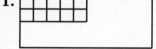

_____40_____

2.

_____30_____

3.

_____100_____

4.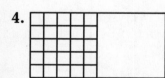

_____50_____

5.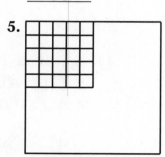

_____100_____

6.

_____75_____

7. Are there more tiles on floor 1 or on floor 4?

_____ floor 4 _____

Harcourt Brace School Publishers

Name _____

Problem-Solving Strategy

Make a Model

Charley has collected a box of acorns. He wants to know about how many acorns are in the box without counting all of them.

Charley decides to make a model. He finds another box the same size. He chooses the benchmark number 25 and puts 25 acorns into the box. He draws a line on the box to show the level of acorns in the box.

Charley uses the benchmark model to guess the number of acorns in the full box.

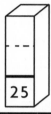

He thinks: The full box has about 3 groups of 25 acorns. 25 + 25 + 25 = 75

Use the benchmark models to estimate the number of items in each full box.

1.

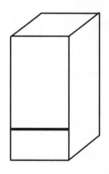 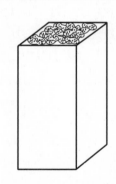

10 peanuts ____40____ peanuts

2.

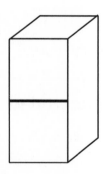 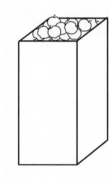

10 crab apples ____20____ crab apples

3.

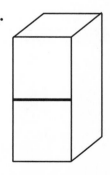 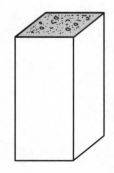

25 pebbles ____50____ pebbles

4.

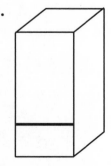 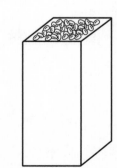

100 pumpkin seeds ____400____ pumpkin seeds

Value of a Digit

The symbols 0, 1, 2, 3, 4, 5, 6, 7, 8, and 9 are called **digits**.

Hundreds	Tens	Ones
5	2	6
500 +	20 +	6
= 526		

In the number 526 the value of the digit 5 is 5 hundreds, or 500. The value of the digit 2 is 2 tens, or 20. The value of the digit 6 is 6 ones, or 6. Read: "five hundred twenty-six"

Example 1

4̲78

The value of the digit 4 is 4 hundreds, or 400.
Say: "four hundred seventy-eight"

Example 2

1̲35

The value of the digit 3 is 3 tens, or 30.
Say: "one hundred thirty-five"

Example 3

629̲

The value of the digit 9 is 9 ones, or 9.
Say: "six hundred twenty-nine"

Example 4

40̲1

A zero in the tens place shows that there are no tens.
Say: "four hundred one"

Write the value of the underlined digit.

1. 125̲

    _____5 ones, or 5_____

2. 6̲58

    _____6 hundreds, or 600_____

3. 41̲6

    _____1 ten, or 10_____

4. 5̲48

    _____5 hundreds, or 500_____

5. 324̲

    _____4 ones, or 4_____

6. 90̲6

    _____0 tens, or 0_____

7. 75̲6

    _____5 tens, or 50_____

8. 2̲30

    _____2 hundreds, or 200_____

9. 427̲

    _____7 ones, or 7_____

10. 64̲3

    _____4 tens, or 40_____

11. 580̲

    _____0 ones, or 0_____

12. 2̲09

    _____2 hundreds, or 200_____

Understanding 1,000's

Understanding large numbers is important for when you read or hear them.

A–C	D–F	G–H	I–J	K–L	M–N	O–Q	R–T	U–W	X–Z
Volume 1	Volume 2	Volume 3	Volume 4	Volume 5	Volume 6	Volume 7	Volume 8	Volume 9	Volume 10
1–100	101–200	201–300	301–400	401–500	501–600	601–700	701–800	801–900	901–1000

Look at the books. If you were looking for page 564, in which volume would you look? You would look in Volume 6 because 564 falls between the numbers 501 and 600.

For Problems 1–5, use the Table of Contents.

1. What subjects are in Chapter 4?

    _____ rocks and _____

    _____ minerals _____

2. John wants to read about the Pacific Ocean. On which pages will he find the information?

    _____ pages 202–299 _____

3. On which page does Chapter 2 begin?

    _____ page 127 _____

Table of Contents	
Chapter 1	
Animals	pp. 3–126
Chapter 2	
Plants	pp. 127–201
Chapter 3	
Oceans	pp. 202–299
Chapter 4	
Rocks and Minerals	pp. 300–463

4. Eileen turns to page 157. What is she reading about?

    _____ plants _____

5. Frank opens the book to page 300. Which chapter did he open to?

    _____ Chapter 4 _____

Patterns of 100's and 1,000's

When you add or subtract a number that ends in zeros, only the first digit changes.

Example 1   274 + 300

2 + 3 = 5, so 274 + 300 = 574

Example 2   689 − 500

6 − 5 = 1, so 689 − 500 = 189

Notice that only the circled digit changed.

Find the sum or difference.

1. 351 + 200   _____551_____   2. 698 + 200   _____898_____

3. 894 − 600   _____294_____   4. 1,235 + 5,000   _____6,235_____

5. 6,987 − 3,000   _____3,987_____   6. 5,000 − 4,000   _____1,000_____

7. 653 + 300   _____953_____   8. 9,546 − 6,000   _____3,546_____

9. 254 + 500   _____754_____   10. 7,231 + 2,000   _____9,231_____

11. 560 − 200   _____360_____   12. 8,556 − 6,000   _____2,556_____

13. 685 + 300   _____985_____   14. 5,456 − 3,000   _____2,456_____

15. 898 − 700   _____198_____   16. 3,425 − 1,000   _____2,425_____

17. 1,346 + 2,000   _____3,346_____   18. 8,450 − 6,000   _____2,450_____

19. 9,423 − 1,000   _____8,423_____   20. 230 + 600   _____830_____

21. Laura had 2,350 stickers. She bought 2,000 more. How many stickers does she have now?

_____ 4,350 stickers _____

Harcourt Brace School Publishers

Understanding 10,000

Ten Thousands	Thousands	Hundreds	Tens	Ones
2	3	6	4	7

2 is in the ten thousands place. Its value is 20,000.

3 is in the thousands place. Its value is 3000.

6 is in the hundreds place. Its value is 600.

4 is in the tens place. Its value is 40.

7 is in the ones place. Its value is 7.

$$20,000 \quad + \quad 3,000 \quad + \quad 600 \quad + \quad 40 \quad + \quad 7$$

You write it: 23,647.

You read it: "twenty-three thousand, six hundred forty-seven."

Write each number.

1. 60,000 + 4,000 + 500 + 90 + 4 _____ 64,594

2. 40,000 + 8,000 + 400 + 70 + 5 _____ 48,475

3. 20,000 + 300 + 50 + 2 _____ 20,352

4. 10,000 + 3,000 + 400 + 40 _____ 13,440

5. 50,000 + 9,000 + 20 + 4 _____ 59,024

6. twenty-two thousand, five hundred forty-three

_____ 22,543 _____

7. thirty-six thousand, two hundred twenty

_____ 36,220 _____

8. fifty-five thousand, three hundred eighty-seven

_____ 55,387 _____

9. ninety thousand, forty

_____ 90,040 _____

10. eighty-three thousand, four hundred seven

_____ 83,407 _____

11. eleven thousand, six hundred sixty-one

_____ 11,661 _____

Using Larger Numbers

When you are using large numbers, it is often helpful to have a starting point to help you understand those large numbers. The starting point is called a **benchmark.** It helps you estimate the size of a number.

For the numbers 1,000 – 9,999, your benchmark would be 1,000.

For the numbers 10,000 – 99,999, your benchmark would be 10,000.

Example 1.   The number of seats in the sports arena is 20,123. The arena is larger than 10,000. The benchmark 10,000 will help you estimate the size of the arena.

Example 2.   The population of Hillside School is 4,986. The school is smaller than 10,000. The benchmark 1,000 will help you estimate the population of Hillside School.

Use the benchmark of 1,000 or 10,000 to estimate the size of each number.

1. 4,568
   1,000

2. 9,123
   1,000

3. 45,123
   10,000

4. 56,187
   10,000

5. 15,679
   10,000

6. 3,510
   1,000

7. 84,659
   10,000

8. 4,391
   1,000

9. 33,516
   10,000

Answer the following questions. Explain your answers.

10. Would you use a benchmark of 1,000 to count the number of chairs in your classroom?

    No; 1,000 would be too large.

11. Would you use a benchmark of 1,000 or 10,000 to count the pencils sold in a year?

    10,000; There are many

    pencils sold each year.

Problem-Solving Strategy

Use a Table

UNDERSTAND your problem. You own an ice cream store. Each of your jumbo freezers holds 10,000 buckets of ice cream. How many freezers will you need to hold the vanilla ice cream?

PLAN You can use a table to help solve your problem.

SOLVE Look at the table. The table shows how much ice cream you ordered. Use the benchmarks of 1,000 and 10,000 to help you find out how many freezers you need.

MY CREAMERY	
Flavors	**Buckets**
Vanilla	30,000
Chocolate	26,000
Coffee	18,750
Strawberry	11,200
Mocha Chip	7,163
Fudge Swirl	4,651

There are three groups of 10,000 in 30,000, so you will need 3 freezers.

For Problems 1–4, use the table.

1. Which color golf ball do people use the most?

   red

2. Each shipping box holds 1,000 balls. How many boxes will be needed to send all the yellow golf balls?

   10 boxes

Colored Golf Balls	
Red	32,956
Blue	20,608
Orange	15,473
Green	15,426
Yellow	9,850
Pink	4,991

3. Which two colors are picked almost the same number of times?

   orange and green

4. Which color golf ball do people use the least?

   pink

Comparing Numbers

Making models with base-ten blocks can help you
compare numbers.

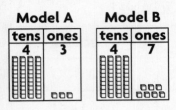

Model A

tens	ones
4	3

Model B

tens	ones
4	7

Model A

hundreds	tens	ones
2	1	4

Model B

hundreds	tens	ones
2	3	2

Step 1 Look at both models.
Compare their place values,
starting from the left.

Step 2 Look in the tens place.
The models are the same, so
continue to compare.

Step 3 Look in the ones place.
The models are not the same.

Step 4 Model B shows more
blocks in the ones place.

So, Model B shows the
greater number.

Step 1 Look at both models.
Compare their place values,
starting from the left.

Step 2 Look in the hundreds
place. The models are the same,
so continue to compare.

Step 3 Look in the tens place.
The models are not the same.

Step 4 Model B shows more
blocks in the tens place.

So, Model B shows the greater
number. (You don't need to
look at the ones since the tens
are different.)

Look at the models below, and write the greater number.

1.
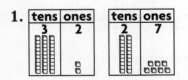

tens	ones
3	2

tens	ones
2	7

_____ 32 _____

2.
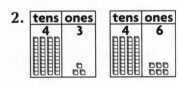

tens	ones
4	3

tens	ones
4	6

_____ 46 _____

3.
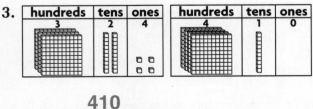

hundreds	tens	ones
3	2	4

hundreds	tens	ones
4	1	0

_____ 410 _____

4.
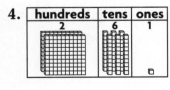

hundreds	tens	ones
2	6	1

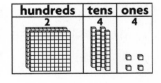

hundreds	tens	ones
2	4	4

_____ 261 _____

More About Comparing Numbers

Compare 421 and 424.

- Look at the digits that have the greatest place value first.

  4̲21   4̲24

- The hundreds are the same, so move right to compare the tens.

  4̲2̲1   4̲2̲4

- The tens are the same, so move right to compare the ones.

  42̲1̲   42̲4̲

- The 4 is greater than the 1, so 424 is greater than 421.

  4 > 1, so 424 > 421

- And, since 1 is less than 4, 421 is less than 424.

  1 < 4, so 421 < 424

- The symbol always points to the smaller number. Examples: 12 < 15; 15 > 12; 132 < 154; 154 > 132.

On the line below each pair of numbers, name the first place value that shows a difference in value.

1. 12   65

_____ tens _____

2. 487   457

_____ tens _____

3. 36   39

_____ ones _____

4. 94   89

_____ tens _____

5. 761   764

_____ ones _____

6. 315   215

_____ hundreds _____

Compare the pairs of numbers below. Write > or < between each pair so that the sign points to the smaller number.

7. 25 (<) 26

8. 78 (<) 95

9. 65 (>) 45

10. 135 (<) 142

11. 357 (<) 359

12. 712 (<) 721

13. 941 (<) 945

14. 256 (>) 125

15. 310 (>) 114

16. 75 (>) 69

17. 236 (<) 246

18. 243 (<) 252

Name _____

Ordering Numbers

When you put more than two numbers in order, you compare the digits, starting with the place value farthest to the left. Set the numbers vertically to help you compare.

Put 351, 352, and 251 in order from least to greatest.

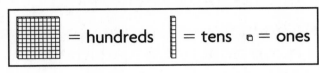
= hundreds   = tens □ = ones

351   352   251

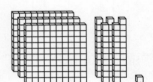 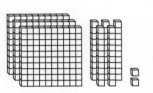 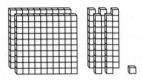

Step 1 Compare the hundreds of all three numbers.
3̲51
3̲52
2̲51
251 has the fewest hundreds, so it has the least value.

Step 2 Compare the tens of the other two numbers.
35̲1
35̲2
There is no difference, so look at the next digit to the right.

Step 3 Now compare the ones.
351̲
352̲
1 < 2, so 351 < 352.

The numbers from least to greatest: 251, 351, 352

Write the numbers from greatest to least. Look at the numbers in the box to help you compare.

1. 265, 387, 254
| 265 |
| 387 |
| 254 |
__387, 265, 254__

2. 126, 654, 349
| 126 |
| 654 |
| 349 |
__654, 349, 126__

3. 458, 455, 465
| 458 |
| 455 |
| 465 |
__465, 458, 455__

4. 23, 46, 15
| 23 |
| 46 |
| 15 |
__46, 23, 15__

5. 78, 84, 74
| 78 |
| 84 |
| 74 |
__84, 78, 74__

6. 112, 212, 115
| 112 |
| 212 |
| 115 |
__212, 115, 112__

Write the numbers from least to greatest. Look at the numbers in the box to help you compare.

7. 65, 89, 64
| 65 |
| 89 |
| 64 |
__64, 65, 89__

8. 450, 458, 397
| 450 |
| 458 |
| 397 |
__397, 450, 458__

9. 263, 223, 323
| 263 |
| 223 |
| 323 |
__223, 263, 323__

Harcourt Brace School Publishers

Problem-Solving Strategy

Draw a Picture

Drawing a picture will help you see what a word problem describes. A number line is a picture.

Heather, Kristen, and Lona guessed how many peanuts were in a bag. Heather guessed 65; Kristen guessed 72; and Lona guessed 54. There were 58 peanuts in the bag. Whose guess was closest?

Draw a number line, and mark the guesses and the correct answer.

Count how many spaces each guess was from the correct answer.

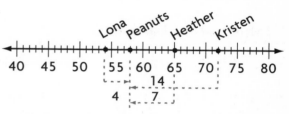

Lona's guess was closest.

Using the number line and the pictures below, answer the following questions.

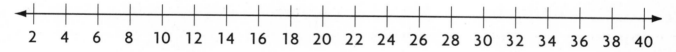

1. Canine Companion dog food comes in three bag sizes: 18, 26, and 36 pounds. Order the bags from smallest to largest.

   18 lb, 26 lb, 36 lb

2. Jessie bought a baseball hat for $13.95, a baseball glove for $23.50 and a baseball for $5.00. Order the items from most to least expensive.

   baseball glove, baseball

   hat, baseball

Rounding to Tens and Hundreds

Rounding to Tens

How do you round numbers like 23 and 26 to tens?

- See what two tens a number falls
between. Both 23 and 26 fall
between 20 and 30.

- See which ten a number is closer to.
If the ones digit is less than 5, round
to the lesser ten. If it is 5 or greater,
round to the greater ten.

$$2\underline{3} \rightarrow 20 \qquad 2\underline{6} \rightarrow 30$$

Rounding to Hundreds

How do you round numbers like 431 and 464 to hundreds?

- See what two hundreds a number falls
between. Both 431 and 464 fall between
400 and 500.

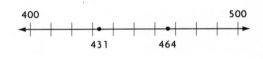

- See which hundred a number is closer
to. If the tens digit is less than 5, round
to the lesser hundred. If it is 5 or greater,
round to the greater hundred.

$$4\underline{3}1 \rightarrow 400 \qquad 4\underline{6}4 \rightarrow 500$$

Round to the nearest ten.

1. 46

2. 52

3. 35

4. 27

___50___

___50___

___40___

___30___

Round to the nearest hundred.

5. 134

6. 782

7. 893

8. 615

___100___

___800___

___900___

___600___

9. 125

10. 675

11. 832

12. 550

___100___

___700___

___800___

___600___

Harcourt Brace School Publishers

More About Rounding

Rounding money is just like rounding tens and hundreds.

Cassandra bought a dress for $**46**. Did the dress cost about $40 or about $50?

You are rounding to tens, so look at the ones digit. Is it less than or greater than 5? Greater; so round up. The dress cost about $50.

$4<u>6</u> → $5<u>0</u>

Jeff bought a lamp for $**235**. Did the lamp cost about $200 or about $300?

You are rounding to hundreds, so look at the tens digit. Is it less than or greater than 5? Less; so round down. The lamp cost about $200.

$2<u>3</u>5 → $2<u>0</u>0

Circle which dollar amount the number rounds to.
Underline the digit that tells you which way to round.

1. $2<u>3</u>

($20) $30

2. $4<u>4</u>

($40) $50

3. $6<u>8</u>

$60   ($70)

4. $3<u>6</u>4

$300   ($400)

5. $4<u>5</u>6

$400   ($500)

6. $4<u>7</u>8

$400   ($500)

Round to the nearest ten dollars. Underline the digit that tells you which way to round.

7. $6<u>2</u>

____$60____

8. $1<u>6</u>

____$20____

9. $9<u>1</u>

____$90____

Round to the nearest hundred dollars. Underline the digit that tells you which way to round.

10. $2<u>1</u>4

____$200____

11. $1<u>2</u>5

____$100____

12. $4<u>7</u>6

____$500____

Making Equal Groups

Max put new wheels on 6 bicycles. How many new wheels did he put on?

You can use counters to answer these questions!

1. Draw a circle underneath each bicycle. How many

   circles did you draw? __6__

2. Draw counters in each circle to show the number of wheels.

   How many counters did you put in each circle? __2__

3. How many counters are there in all? __12__

4. How many wheels did Max put on? __12__

Make a model to answer each question.

5. Morgan polishes 6 sets of silverware. There are 5 pieces in each set. How many pieces does she polish?

   __30 pieces__

6. Each relay team has 5 runners. There are 8 teams in the race. How many runners are there in all?

   __40 runners__

7. Mrs. Shaw bought 3 bags of 12 oranges. How many oranges did she buy?

   __36 oranges__

8. Stella has 3 vases. She cuts 6 roses for each vase. How many roses does she cut?

   __18 roses__

9. On Monday, Ed shoes 4 horses. How many horseshoes does he put on?

   __16 horseshoes__

10. There are 8 pairs of sneakers in the gym. How many sneakers are there in all?

    __16 sneakers__

Harcourt Brace School Publishers

Multiplying with 2 and 5

Byron needs to pack 5 pairs of socks for vacation. He rolls his socks into pairs and places them in his suitcase, one pair at a time: $2 + 2 + 2 + 2 + 2 = 10$.

Then, worried that he's made a mistake, he takes them out, one pair at a time, and skip counts: 2, 4, 6, 8, 10.

Then, he multiplies his **factors** (2 socks times 5 pairs) as he puts his **product** (10 socks) back in his suitcase: $2 \times 5 = 10$.

Solve each problem by adding, then by skip counting, and then by multiplying.

1. There are 4 houses on Dix Street, and each house has 5 bedrooms. How many bedrooms are there on Dix Street?

$5 + 5 + 5 + 5 = 20;$

$5, 10, 15, 20;$

$4 \times 5 = 20$

_____

2. The Sampson children left 3 pairs of muddy boots on the steps. How many muddy boots are there?

$2 + 2 + 2 = 6;$

$2, 4, 6;$

$3 \times 2 = 6$

_____

3. Angelo has lost 2 buttons from each of his 6 dress shirts. How many buttons are missing?

$2 + 2 + 2 + 2 + 2$
$+ 2 = 12;$

$2, 4, 6, 8, 10, 12;$

$6 \times 2 = 12$

Name _____

Problem-Solving Strategy

Draw a Picture

THE PROBLEM

At practice, (8 batters) practice their hitting. Each batter swings at (5 pitches.) How many swings in all are made?

UNDERSTAND

1. Underline what the problem asks.

2. Circle the information you will use to answer the question.

PLAN

3. Circle the strategy that you can use to solve the problem.

    a. Act It Out   **b.** (Draw a Picture)   **c.** Find a Pattern

SOLVE

4. Draw 8 circles to represent the batters. Put 5 dots in each circle to represent the pitches.

5. How many dots are there in all? __40__

6. How many pitches are thrown? __40__

Draw a picture to solve the problem. Remember to understand and plan before you solve.

7. The Tigers scored 2 runs in each inning of a game. If the game was 6 innings long, how many runs did the Tigers score?

            12 runs

8. Molly's 6 sisters are saving money to buy her a gift. If each sister saves $3, how much money will they have for her gift?

            $18

Multiplying with 3

The Wings and the Hawks practiced for a championship soccer game.

The Wings practiced 3 hours a day for 4 days. Use the number line to see how many hours they practiced in all.

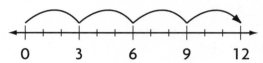

The Hawks practiced 4 hours a day for 3 days. How many hours did they practice in all?

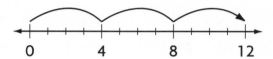

1. What multiplication sentence is shown on the number line?

    _____ 4 × 3 = 12 _____

2. What multiplication sentence is shown on the number line?

    _____ 3 × 4 = 12 _____

3. How many hours did the Wings practice in all?

    _____ 12 hr _____

4. How many hours did the Hawks practice in all?

    _____ 12 hr _____

5. Look at Exercises 1–4 above. They show the **Order Property of Multiplication**. They show that the

    products of _____ 3 × 4 _____ and _____ 4 × 3 _____

    are both equal to _____ 12 _____ .

Use number lines to solve these problems.

6. Mia drove 3 hours a day for 6 days. How many hours did she drive?

    _____ 18 hr _____

7. Ted drove 6 hours a day for 3 days. How many hours did he drive?

    _____ 18 hr _____

8. Fran earned $5 a week for 3 weeks. How did she earn in all?

    _____ $15 _____

9. Graham earned $3 a week for 5 weeks. How much did he earn in all?

    _____ $15 _____

Multiplying with 1 and 0

- Pam put 1 muffin in each of 6 bags. How many muffins did she put in the bags?

You can draw a picture to find the answer.

Draw 6 bags, with 1 muffin in each bag.

1. What multiplication sentence can you write for

   6 bags with 1 muffin in each bag? ___$6 \times 1 = 6$___

2. What happens when you multiply any number by 1?

   ___The product is the number being multiplied.___

- Pam gave each bag holding a muffin to a friend. Each friend ate the muffin. Now how many muffins are there?

You can draw another picture to find the answer.

Draw 6 empty bags, 0 muffins in each.

3. What multiplication sentence can you write for

   6 bags with 0 muffins in each bag? ___$6 \times 0 = 0$___

4. What happens when you multiply any number by 0?

   ___The product is 0.___

Find the product.

5. $1 \times 9 =$ __9__   6. $0 \times 6 =$ __0__   7. $8 \times 0 =$ __0__   8. $5 \times 1 =$ __5__

9. $7 \times 1 =$ __7__   10. $0 \times 0 =$ __0__   11. $3 \times 1 =$ __3__   12. $9 \times 0 =$ __0__

13. $1 \times 4 =$ __4__   14. $0 \times 2 =$ __0__   15. $6 \times 1 =$ __6__   16. $5 \times 0 =$ __0__

Multiplying with 4

Nate counted his baseball cards. He made 9 stacks with 4 cards in each stack. How many cards did he have?

You can use a multiplication table to find the number of cards.

Step 1 Nate has 9 stacks of cards. So, 9 is a factor. Find the row marked 9.

Step 2 There are 4 cards in each stack. So, 4 is a factor. Find the column marked 4.

Step 3 Find the box where row 9 and column 4 meet. This box shows the product of 9 and 4.

×	0	1	2	3	4	5	6	7	8	9
0	0	0	0	0	0	0	0	0	0	0
1	0	1	2	3	4	5	6	7	8	9
2	0	2	4	6	8	10	12	14	16	18
3	0	3	6	9	12	15	18	21	24	27
4	0	4	8	12	16	20	24	28	32	36
5	0	5	10	15	20	25	30	35	40	45
6	0	6	12	18	24	30	36	42	48	54
7	0	7	14	21	28	35	42	49	56	63
8	0	8	16	24	32	40	48	56	64	72
9	0	9	18	27	36	45	54	63	72	81

Using the multiplication table, you find that Nate had 36 cards.

Name the factors in each of the problems below. Then, use the multiplication table to solve.

1. Mia uses 7 ribbons on every card she makes. Mia wants to make 4 cards. How many ribbons does she need?

   Factors: _____ 7, 4;

   _____ 28 ribbons

2. Akio gets an allowance of $4 each week. He spends $3 and saves the rest. How much does he save every 8 weeks?

   Factors: _____ 1, 8;

   _____ $8

3. Norman practices basketball 1 hour on school days and 2 hours each day of the weekend. How many hours does he practice in 4 weeks?

   Factors: _____ 9, 4;

   _____ 36 hours

4. Tamisha counted the dimes in her bank. She made 6 stacks with 4 dimes in each stack. How many dimes did she count?

   Factors: _____ 6, 4;

   _____ 24 dimes

Modeling Multiplication 0–6

An **array** shows objects in rows and columns.
An array can be used to show a multiplication sentence.

Show 3 × 6.

The array has 3 rows.
Each row has 6 circles.

3 × 6 = 18

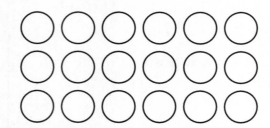

Complete the number sentence to show how many in all.

1.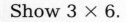

3 × 5 = ___15___

2.

4 × 3 = ___12___

3.

5 × 6 = ___30___

Draw the array for each exercise below.
Write the product. **Check students' drawings.**

4. 5 rows of 2

5. 4 rows of 4

6. 6 rows of 4

5 × 2 = ___10___

4 × 4 = ___16___

6 × 4 = ___24___

7. 2 rows of 6

8. 4 rows of 5

9. 3 rows of 3

2 × 6 = ___12___

4 × 5 = ___20___

3 × 3 = ___9___

Multiplying with 7

You can multiply two numbers in either order.
The product is the same.

Find 3 × 7.

✖ ✖ ✖ ✖ ✖ ✖   7 × 1 = 7
✖ ✖ ✖ ✖ ✖ ✖   7 × 2 = 14
✖ ✖ ✖ ✖ ✖ ✖   7 × 3 = 21

3 rows of 7
3 × 7 = 21

Find 7 × 3.

✖ ✖ ✖   3 × 1 = 3
✖ ✖ ✖   3 × 2 = 6
✖ ✖ ✖   3 × 3 = 9
✖ ✖ ✖   3 × 4 = 12
✖ ✖ ✖   3 × 5 = 15
✖ ✖ ✖   3 × 6 = 18
✖ ✖ ✖   3 × 7 = 21

7 rows of 3
7 × 3 = 21

Complete the number sentences.

1. ✖ ✖ ✖ ✖ ✖ ✖ ✖   ✖ ✖
    ✖ ✖ ✖ ✖ ✖ ✖ ✖   ✖ ✖
                        ✖ ✖
    2 × 7 = __14__   ✖ ✖
                        ✖ ✖
                        ✖ ✖
                        ✖ ✖

    7 × 2 = __14__

2. ✖ ✖ ✖ ✖ ✖ ✖ ✖   ✖ ✖ ✖ ✖
    ✖ ✖ ✖ ✖ ✖ ✖ ✖   ✖ ✖ ✖ ✖
    ✖ ✖ ✖ ✖ ✖ ✖ ✖   ✖ ✖ ✖ ✖
    ✖ ✖ ✖ ✖ ✖ ✖ ✖   ✖ ✖ ✖ ✖
                        ✖ ✖ ✖ ✖
    4 × 7 = __28__   ✖ ✖ ✖ ✖
                        ✖ ✖ ✖ ✖

                        7 × 4 = __28__

Find the product for each pair of factors.

3. $\begin{array}{r} 7 \\ \times 1 \\ \hline 7 \end{array}$ $\begin{array}{r} 1 \\ \times 7 \\ \hline 7 \end{array}$

4. $\begin{array}{r} 7 \\ \times 8 \\ \hline 56 \end{array}$ $\begin{array}{r} 8 \\ \times 7 \\ \hline 56 \end{array}$

5. $\begin{array}{r} 7 \\ \times 6 \\ \hline 42 \end{array}$ $\begin{array}{r} 6 \\ \times 7 \\ \hline 42 \end{array}$

6. $\begin{array}{r} 7 \\ \times 5 \\ \hline 35 \end{array}$ $\begin{array}{r} 5 \\ \times 7 \\ \hline 35 \end{array}$

7. $\begin{array}{r} 7 \\ \times 9 \\ \hline 63 \end{array}$ $\begin{array}{r} 9 \\ \times 7 \\ \hline 63 \end{array}$

8. $\begin{array}{r} 7 \\ \times 0 \\ \hline 0 \end{array}$ $\begin{array}{r} 0 \\ \times 7 \\ \hline 0 \end{array}$

9. $\begin{array}{r} 7 \\ \times 3 \\ \hline 21 \end{array}$ $\begin{array}{r} 3 \\ \times 7 \\ \hline 21 \end{array}$

10. $\begin{array}{r} 7 \\ \times 4 \\ \hline 28 \end{array}$ $\begin{array}{r} 4 \\ \times 7 \\ \hline 28 \end{array}$

Name _____

LESSON
12.3

Multiplying with 8

You can use the multiplication facts you know to learn new facts. The examples show two different ways to learn 6×8.

5×8 ▦ 40 | 3×8 ▦ 24

$\underline{+ 1 \times 8}$ ▦ $\underline{+ 8}$ | $\underline{+ 3 \times 8}$ ▦ $\underline{+ 24}$

$6 \times 8 \quad = \quad 48$ | $6 \times 8 \quad = \quad 48$

Complete the equations.

1. ▦ $3 \times 8 = \underline{24}$ 2. ▦ $2 \times 8 = \underline{16}$

   ▦ $1 \times 8 = \underline{8}$ ▦ $2 \times 8 = \underline{16}$

   $4 \times 8 = \underline{32}$ $4 \times 8 = \underline{32}$

Find the product. You may use the facts that are given to help you.

3. $5 \times 8 = 40$ 4. $4 \times 8 = 32$ 5. $3 \times 8 = 24$ 6. $7 \times 8 = 56$

   $1 \times 8 = 8$ $1 \times 8 = 8$ $3 \times 8 = 24$ $2 \times 8 = 16$

   $6 \times 8 = \underline{48}$ $5 \times 8 = \underline{40}$ $6 \times 8 = \underline{48}$ $9 \times 8 = \underline{72}$

Find the product for each pair of factors.

7. $\begin{array}{r} 8 \\ \times 7 \\ \hline 56 \end{array}$ $\begin{array}{r} 7 \\ \times 8 \\ \hline 56 \end{array}$ 8. $\begin{array}{r} 8 \\ \times 5 \\ \hline 40 \end{array}$ $\begin{array}{r} 5 \\ \times 8 \\ \hline 40 \end{array}$ 9. $\begin{array}{r} 8 \\ \times 9 \\ \hline 72 \end{array}$ $\begin{array}{r} 9 \\ \times 8 \\ \hline 72 \end{array}$ 10. $\begin{array}{r} 8 \\ \times 3 \\ \hline 24 \end{array}$ $\begin{array}{r} 3 \\ \times 8 \\ \hline 24 \end{array}$

11. $\begin{array}{r} 4 \\ \times 8 \\ \hline 32 \end{array}$ $\begin{array}{r} 8 \\ \times 4 \\ \hline 32 \end{array}$ 12. $\begin{array}{r} 0 \\ \times 8 \\ \hline 0 \end{array}$ $\begin{array}{r} 8 \\ \times 0 \\ \hline 0 \end{array}$ 13. $\begin{array}{r} 6 \\ \times 8 \\ \hline 48 \end{array}$ $\begin{array}{r} 8 \\ \times 6 \\ \hline 48 \end{array}$ 14. $\begin{array}{r} 2 \\ \times 8 \\ \hline 16 \end{array}$ $\begin{array}{r} 8 \\ \times 2 \\ \hline 16 \end{array}$

R68   TAKE ANOTHER LOOK

Harcourt Brace School Publishers

Multiplying with 9

You can learn facts of 9 by comparing them with
facts of 10.

Find 4 × 9.

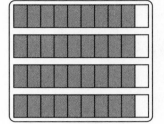

$4 \times 10 = 40$

$40 - 4 = 36$

$4 \times 9 = 36$

Find 6 × 9.

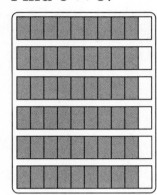

$6 \times 10 = 60$

$60 - 6 = 54$

$6 \times 9 = 54$

Complete the equations.

1. $7 \times 10 = \underline{\;70\;}$

   $70 - 7 = \underline{\;63\;}$

   $7 \times 9 = \underline{\;63\;}$

2. $2 \times 10 = \underline{\;20\;}$

   $20 - 2 = \underline{\;18\;}$

   $2 \times 9 = \underline{\;18\;}$

3. $5 \times 10 = \underline{\;50\;}$

   $50 - 5 = \underline{\;45\;}$

   $5 \times 9 = \underline{\;45\;}$

4. $3 \times 10 = \underline{\;30\;}$

   $30 - 3 = \underline{\;27\;}$

   $3 \times 9 = \underline{\;27\;}$

5. $8 \times 10 = \underline{\;80\;}$

   $80 - 8 = \underline{\;72\;}$

   $8 \times 9 = \underline{\;72\;}$

6. $9 \times 10 = \underline{\;90\;}$

   $90 - 9 = \underline{\;81\;}$

   $9 \times 9 = \underline{\;81\;}$

Find the product.

7. $\begin{array}{r} 9 \\ \times 4 \\ \hline 36 \end{array}$

8. $\begin{array}{r} 9 \\ \times 7 \\ \hline 63 \end{array}$

9. $\begin{array}{r} 9 \\ \times 3 \\ \hline 27 \end{array}$

10. $\begin{array}{r} 9 \\ \times 8 \\ \hline 72 \end{array}$

11. $\begin{array}{r} 9 \\ \times 5 \\ \hline 45 \end{array}$

12. $\begin{array}{r} 9 \\ \times 6 \\ \hline 54 \end{array}$

13. $\begin{array}{r} 2 \\ \times 9 \\ \hline 18 \end{array}$

14. $\begin{array}{r} 7 \\ \times 9 \\ \hline 63 \end{array}$

15. $\begin{array}{r} 5 \\ \times 9 \\ \hline 45 \end{array}$

16. $\begin{array}{r} 9 \\ \times 9 \\ \hline 81 \end{array}$

17. $\begin{array}{r} 4 \\ \times 9 \\ \hline 36 \end{array}$

18. $\begin{array}{r} 8 \\ \times 9 \\ \hline 72 \end{array}$

Problem-Solving Strategy

Make a Model

You can make a model to solve problems.

A large window is made up of square panes. The window is 3 panes high and 6 panes wide. How many panes make up the large window?

Use tiles to make a model of the window. Use one tile for each pane.

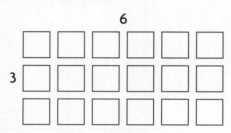

3 rows of 6 panes

$3 \times 6 = 18$

So, the large window has 18 panes.

Make a model using tiles or counters. Solve.

1. Steven bought a sheet of stickers. There are 5 rows of stickers. There are 6 stickers in each row. How many stickers did Steven buy?

   30 stickers

2. Mary is putting her model cars on her shelves. She puts 4 models on each shelf. There are 4 shelves. How many models in all are there?

   16 models

3. The baker arranged cupcakes on a tray. He made 4 rows of cupcakes, with 6 cupcakes in each row. How many cupcakes in all are there?

   24 cupcakes

4. Dennis found an old United States flag. He counted 6 rows of stars. There are 8 stars in each row. How many stars are on the flag?

   48 stars

Harcourt Brace School Publishers

Completing the Multiplication Table

On a multiplication table, you record a product where a row and a column meet.

Example: $3 \times 5 = 15$
Record 15 where row 3 and column 5 meet.

Note: You can check your products. Check the rows and columns one by one. Each row and column should show the multiplication table for the number at the head of the row or column.

column

X	1	2	3	4	5	6
1						
2						
3					15	
4						
5						
6						

row →

Activity

You will need two number cubes.

- Roll the number cubes and find the product of the two numbers.

- Record the product on the multiplication table in just **one** place.

  Example: Suppose you roll ⚃ and ⚀.

  You may record the product 8 where row 4 and column 2 meet, **or** where row 2 and column 4 meet.

- Keep playing until you have recorded at least two numbers in each row.

- Then fill in the remaining numbers on the table and check your work.

  Check students' tables.

X	1	2	3	4	5	6
1	1	2	3	4	5	6
2	2	4	6	8	10	12
3	3	6	9	12	15	18
4	4	8	12	16	20	24
5	5	10	15	20	25	30
6	6	12	18	24	30	36

Exploring Division

Use division when you want to separate objects into groups of equal size.

You have 12 marbles.

You want to make 3 groups of equal size.

You put 4 marbles in each group.

Say: 12 divided by 3 equals 4.
Write: 12 ÷ 3 = 4

Solve.

1.

How many in all? __12__

How many groups? __2__

How many in each group? __6__

12 ÷ 2 = __6__

2.

How many in all? __12__

How many groups? __6__

How many in each group? __2__

12 ÷ 6 = __2__

3.

How many in all? __8__

How many groups? __2__

How many in each group? __4__

8 ÷ 2 = __4__

4.

How many in all? __8__

How many groups? __4__

How many in each group? __2__

8 ÷ 4 = __2__

Connecting Subtraction and Division

Division is like repeated subtraction.

How many groups of 2 are there in 8?

Start at 8 on the number line.
Count back 2 spaces at a time until you reach 0.

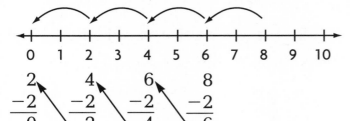

You can subtract 2 from 8 four times because there are
4 equal groups of 2 in 8.

$8 \div 2 = 4$

Find the quotient. You may use the number line to help.

1. $12 \div 2 = \underline{\ 6\ }$

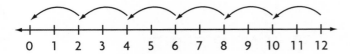

2. $12 \div 6 = \underline{\ 2\ }$

3. $12 \div 3 = \underline{\ 4\ }$

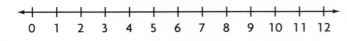

4. $12 \div 4 = \underline{\ 3\ }$

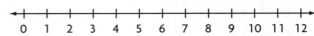

5. $10 \div 2 = \underline{\ 5\ }$

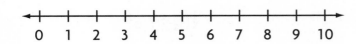

6. $10 \div 5 = \underline{\ 2\ }$

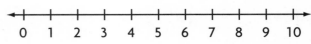

7. $9 \div 3 = \underline{\ 3\ }$

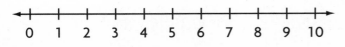

8. $8 \div 4 = \underline{\ 2\ }$

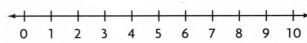

Name _____

Relating Multiplication and Division

Multiplication and division are related.

Division is the **inverse**, or opposite, of multiplication.

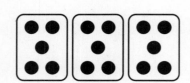

3 groups of 5 equal 15 in all.

$$3 \quad \times \quad 5 \quad = \quad 15$$
  ↑   ↑   ↑
factor   factor   product

15 divides into 3 equal groups of 5

$$15 \quad \div \quad 3 \quad = \quad 5$$
  ↑   ↑   ↑
dividend divisor quotient

Write the missing number for each number sentence.

1.

$4 \times \underline{\ 3\ } = 12$

$12 \div 4 = \underline{\ 3\ }$

2.

$3 \times \underline{\ 4\ } = 12$

$12 \div 3 = \underline{\ 4\ }$

3.

$6 \times \underline{\ 3\ } = 18$

$18 \div 6 = \underline{\ 3\ }$

4.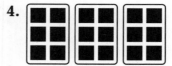

$3 \times \underline{\ 6\ } = 18$

$18 \div 3 = \underline{\ 6\ }$

Complete.

5. $4 \times \underline{\ 5\ } = 20$, so $20 \div 4 = \underline{\ 5\ }$

6. $4 \times \underline{\ 4\ } = 16$, so $16 \div 4 = \underline{\ 4\ }$

7. $3 \times \underline{\ 5\ } = 15$, so $15 \div 3 = \underline{\ 5\ }$

8. $5 \times \underline{\ 6\ } = 30$, so $30 \div 5 = \underline{\ 6\ }$

9. $2 \times \underline{\ 8\ } = 16$, so $16 \div 2 = \underline{\ 8\ }$

10. $7 \times \underline{\ 3\ } = 21$, so $21 \div 7 = \underline{\ 3\ }$

11. $3 \times \underline{\ 3\ } = 9$, so $9 \div 3 = \underline{\ 3\ }$

12. $5 \times \underline{\ 7\ } = 35$, so $35 \div 5 = \underline{\ 7\ }$

Harcourt Brace School Publishers

Fact Families

Use multiplication and division to tell about the cookies
in opposite ways.

Use multiplication to
put same-size groups
together.

$3 \times 4 = 12$
or
$4 \times 3 = 12$

Use division to separate
the total into same-size
groups.

$12 \div 3 = 4$
or
$12 \div 4 = 3$

The four number sentences are called a **fact family**.
Each of the four sentences uses the same numbers.

Complete each fact family.

1.

$2 \times 4 = 8$

$4 \times 2 = 8$

$8 \div 2 = 4$

$8 \div 4 = 2$

2.

$3 \times 2 = 6$

$2 \times 3 = 6$

$6 \div 3 = 2$

$6 \div 2 = 3$

3.

$3 \times 5 = 15$

$5 \times 3 = 15$

$15 \div 3 = 5$

$15 \div 5 = 3$

4.

$6 \times 3 = 18$

$3 \times 6 = 18$

$18 \div 6 = 3$

$18 \div 3 = 6$

5.

$6 \times 4 = 24$

$4 \times 6 = 24$

$24 \div 6 = 4$

$24 \div 4 = 6$

6.

$7 \times 3 = 21$

$3 \times 7 = 21$

$21 \div 7 = 3$

$21 \div 3 = 7$

Practicing Division Facts Through 5

You can use a multiplication table to find a missing factor.

×	2	3	4	5	6	7
2	4	6	8	10	12	14
3	6	9	12	15	18	21
4	8	12	16	20	24	28
5	10	15	20	25	30	35
6	12	18	24	30	36	42
7	14	21	28	35	42	49

missing
factor   factor   product
↓   ↓   ↓

$$\underline{?} \times 4 = 24$$

1. Find the known factor, **4**, in the top row.

2. Look down to find the product, **24**.

3. Look left to find the missing factor, **6**.

You can use the same process to find a quotient.

1. Find the divisor, **4**, in the top row.

2. Look down to find the dividend, **24**.

3. Look left to find the quotient, **6**.

So, $6 \times 4 = 24$, and $24 \div 4 = 6$.

dividend   divisor   quotient
↓   ↓   ↓

$$24 \div 4 = ?$$

Find the missing factor or quotient. You may use the mutiplication table.

1. $\underline{2} \times 5 = 10$ 2. $\underline{6} \times 3 = 18$ 3. $\underline{4} \times 4 = 16$

4. $\underline{4} \times 5 = 20$ 5. $\underline{3} \times 4 = 12$ 6. $\underline{3} \times 7 = 21$

7. $28 \div 4 = \underline{7}$ 8. $36 \div 6 = \underline{6}$ 9. $25 \div 5 = \underline{5}$

Complete the table. The top row lists the dividends and the left column lists the divisor.

10.

÷	4	6	8	10	12
2	2	3	4	5	6

11.

÷	10	15	20	25	30
5	2	3	4	5	6

Harcourt Brace School Publishers

Name _____

Choosing Division or Multiplication

Drawing a picture can help you choose which operation to use to solve a problem.

Problem	Solution
There are 3 fish bowls. There are 4 fish in each bowl. How many fish are there in all?	**Multiply.** You know the number of same-size groups and the number in each group. You need to find the total. $3 \times 4 = 12$
There are 6 mice. You want to separate the mice equally in 2 cages. How many mice should you put in each cage?	**Divide.** You know the total and the number of same-size groups. You need to find the number in each group. $6 \div 2 = 3$
There are 8 kittens. You want to put 2 kittens in each basket. How many baskets do you need?	**Divide.** You know the total and the number in each same-size group. You need to find the number of groups. $8 \div 2 = 4$

Write a number sentence and solve. You may draw a picture.

1. Mary picked 12 apples. She put 3 apples in each basket. How many baskets did she use?

   $12 \div 3 = 4;$ **4 baskets**

2. If 4 friends shared 20 crayons equally, how many crayons did each friend get?

   $20 \div 4 = 5;$ **5 crayons**

3. Mrs. Jones bought 3 packages of muffins, with 6 muffins in each package. How many muffins did she buy in all?

   $3 \times 6 = 18;$ **18 muffins**

4. A classroom has 4 tables, with 6 chairs at each table. How many chairs are there in all?

   $4 \times 6 = 24;$ **24 chairs**

Harcourt Brace School Publishers

Problem-Solving Strategy

Write a Number Sentence

You can write a number sentence to help you solve a problem.

Example: There are 18 students in Josh's class. They are working in groups of 3. How many groups are there in all?

$$18 \div 3 = 6$$

number of students   number in each group   number of groups

Remember

Multiply

- when you are joining groups of equal size.

- when you know the size of the groups and the number of same-size groups.

Divide

- when you are separating a total into groups of equal size.

- when you know the total.

- when you know either the number of same-size groups or the number in each group.

Write a number sentence to solve. Then write the answer.

1. Mary rode her bicycle 4 miles every day for 5 days. How many miles did she ride in all?

    $5 \times 4 = 20$

    20 mi

2. Twelve campers want to canoe. Each canoe holds 3 people. How many canoes are needed?

    $12 \div 3 = 4$

    4 canoes

3. Jeff earns $3 an hour for raking leaves. How many hours does he need to work to earn $15?

    $15 \div 3 = 5$

    5 hr

4. Jackie made a cartoon book that is 8 pages long. There are 4 cartoons on each page. How many cartoons are in the book?

    $8 \times 4 = 32$

    32 cartoons

Harcourt Brace School Publishers

Name _____

Modeling Division Using Arrays

Find how many equal groups of 5 are in 15. Find 15 ÷ 5.

Step 1

Use 15 tiles.

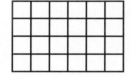

Step 2

Place 5 tiles in each row.

Use all the tiles.

Step 3

Count the rows of 5.

There are 3 rows of 5.

15 ÷ 5 = 3

The array shows → two division facts:

There are 3 equal groups of 5 in 15. → 15 ÷ 5 = 3

There are 5 equal groups of 3 in 15. → 15 ÷ 3 = 5

Complete the division sentences.

1.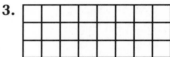

24 ÷ 6 = __4__

24 ÷ 4 = __6__

2.

10 ÷ 2 = __5__

10 ÷ 5 = __2__

3.

24 ÷ 8 = __3__

24 ÷ 3 = __8__

Write two division sentences for each array.

4.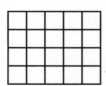

20 ÷ 5 = 4

20 ÷ 4 = 5

5.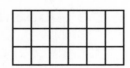

18 ÷ 6 = 3

18 ÷ 3 = 6

6.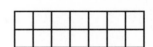

14 ÷ 7 = 2

14 ÷ 2 = 7

Dividing Using 0 and 1

$6 \div 6 = ?$	$6 \div 1 = ?$	$0 \div 6 = ?$
Divide 6 counters into groups of 6.	Divide 6 counters into groups of 1.	Divide 0 counters into groups of 6.

There is 1 group.	There are 6 groups.	There are 0 groups
$6 \div 6 = 1$	$6 \div 1 = 6$	$0 \div 6 = 0$

Any number divided by itself is 1.	Any number divided by 1 is that number.	Zero divided by any number is 0.

Find the quotient.

1. $8 \div 8 =$ △1

2. $4 \div 1 =$ ④

3. $0 \div 5 =$ ⬜0

4. $7 \div 1 =$ ⑦

5. $3 \div 3 =$ △1

6. $9 \div 9 =$ △1

7. $0 \div 3 =$ ⬜0

8. $1 \div 1 =$ ①

9. $0 \div 7 =$ ⬜0

10. $8 \div 1 =$ ⑧

11. $2 \div 2 =$ △1

12. $4 \div 4 =$ △1

13. $7 \div 7 =$ △1

14. $5 \div 1 =$ ⑤

15. $0 \div 2 =$ ⬜0

Look at Exercises 1–15 again. If a number is divided by itself, put a triangle around the quotient. If a number is divided by 1, put a circle around the quotient. If the dividend is 0, put a box around the quotient.

Find the missing factor.

16. $1 \times \underline{8} = 8$

17. $7 \times \underline{0} = 0$

18. $1 \times \underline{5} = 5$

19. $\underline{0} \times 8 = 0$

20. $4 \times \underline{1} = 4$

21. $\underline{3} \times 1 = 3$

22. $\underline{1} \times 3 = 3$

23. $\underline{0} \times 3 = 0$

24. $6 \times \underline{1} = 6$

Using the Multiplication Table to Divide

You can use a multiplication table to find a missing factor or a quotient.

Find $56 \div 8$.

Think of the missing factor in the related multiplication sentence.

missing
factor   factor   product
  ↓   ↓   ↓
  ?   ×   8   =   56

×	0	1	2	3	4	5	6	7	8	9
0	0	0	0	0	0	0	0	0	0	0
1	0	1	2	3	4	5	6	7	8	9
2	0	2	4	6	8	10	12	14	16	18
3	0	3	6	9	12	15	18	21	24	27
4	0	4	8	12	16	20	24	28	32	36
5	0	5	10	15	20	25	30	35	40	45
6	0	6	12	18	24	30	36	42	48	54
7	0	7	14	21	28	35	42	49	56	63
8	0	8	16	24	32	40	48	56	64	72
9	0	9	18	27	36	45	54	63	72	81

1. Find the factor **8** in the top row.

2. Look down to find the product **56**.

3. Look left to find the missing factor, **7**.

So, **7** × 8 = 56, and 56 ÷ 8 = **7**.

Find the missing factor. You may use the multiplication table.

1. __2__ × 5 = 10   2. __5__ × 8 = 40   3. __4__ × 4 = 16

4. __8__ × 8 = 64   5. __0__ × 6 = 0   6. __1__ × 7 = 7

7. __9__ × 5 = 45   8. __8__ × 4 = 32   9. __6__ × 7 = 42

10. 7 × __4__ = 28   11. 6 × __4__ = 24   12. 9 × __7__ = 63

Find the quotient. You may use the multiplication table.

13. 42 ÷ 7 = __6__   14. 54 ÷ 6 = __9__   15. 14 ÷ 2 = __7__

16. 36 ÷ 4 = __9__   17. 35 ÷ 5 = __7__   18. 27 ÷ 3 = __9__

19. 12 ÷ 4 = __3__   20. 0 ÷ 6 = __0__   21. 72 ÷ 9 = __8__

22. 24 ÷ 6 = __4__   23. 28 ÷ 4 = __7__   24. 8 ÷ 8 = __1__

25. 20 ÷ 4 = __5__   26. 48 ÷ 6 = __8__   27. 64 ÷ 8 = __8__

Practicing Division Facts Through 9

One way to recall a division fact is to think of a related multiplication fact.

Find $18 \div 3$.

Think: How many groups of 3 are in 18? —or—
What number multiplied times 3 equals 18?

$? \times 3 = 18$

$6 \times 3 = 18$, so $18 \div 3 = 6$.

Complete.

1. __6__ $\times 4 = 24$, so $24 \div 4 = $ __6__   2. __3__ $\times 9 = 27$, so $27 \div 9 = $ __3__

3. __7__ $\times 5 = 35$, so $35 \div 5 = $ __7__   4. __6__ $\times 6 = 36$, so $36 \div 6 = $ __6__

5. __4__ $\times 8 = 32$, so $32 \div 8 = $ __4__   6. __3__ $\times 7 = 21$, so $21 \div 7 = $ __3__

Find the quotient. Think about multiplication facts that have 5 as a factor.

7. $25 \div 5 = $ __5__   8. $40 \div 5 = $ __8__   9. $15 \div 5 = $ __3__

10. $10 \div 5 = $ __2__   11. $45 \div 5 = $ __9__   12. $20 \div 5 = $ __4__

13. $35 \div 5 = $ __7__   14. $5 \div 5 = $ __1__   15. $30 \div 5 = $ __6__

Find the quotient. Think about multiplication facts that have 9 as a factor.

16. $63 \div 9 = $ __7__   17. $72 \div 9 = $ __8__   18. $18 \div 9 = $ __2__

19. $45 \div 9 = $ __5__   20. $27 \div 9 = $ __3__   21. $54 \div 9 = $ __6__

22. $9 \div 9 = $ __1__   23. $36 \div 9 = $ __4__   24. $81 \div 9 = $ __9__

Problem-Solving Strategy

Make a Table

Mr. Hill is making model cars. He needs 4 wheels for each car. He has 20 wheels. How many cars can he make?

You can *make a table* to help solve this problem.

Wheels	4	8	12	16	20
Cars	1	2	3	4	5

The table shows that, with 20 wheels, Mr. Hill can make 5 cars.

Complete the table to solve each problem.

1. Tony is going to camp for 28 days. How many weeks is this?

   _____ 4 weeks _____

Days	7	14	21	28
Weeks	1	2	3	4

2. It takes Mary 2 minutes to wash 8 dishes. How many dishes can she wash in 12 minutes?

   _____ 48 dishes _____

Minutes	2	4	6	8	10	12
Dishes	8	16	24	32	40	48

3. The baker needs 3 eggs to make a cake. How many cakes can he make with 12 eggs?

   _____ 4 cakes _____

Eggs	3	6	9	12
Cakes	1	2	3	4

4. Muffins are sold in packages of 6. Mrs. Jones wants 30 muffins for a breakfast party. How many packages should she buy?

   _____ 5 packages _____

Muffins	6	12	18	24	30
Packages	1	2	3	4	5

Choosing the Operation

The table below shows examples of problems in which
you add, subtract, multiply, or divide.

There are 18 children and 6 adults at the park. How many people are at the park?	**Add** — You are joining groups of different size. $18 + 6 = 24$ 24 people
There are 10 boys and 8 girls at the park. How many more boys are there than girls?	**Subtract** — You are comparing two different amounts. $10 - 8 = 2$ 2 more boys
There are 3 sets of swings. Each swing set has 4 swings. How many swings are there in all?	**Multiply** — You are joining groups of equal size. $3 \times 4 = 12$ 12 swings
The 18 students in a class divide into teams of 6 to play a game. How many teams of students are there?	**Divide** — You are separating a total into groups of equal size. $18 \div 6 = 3$ 3 teams

Choose the operation you need to use. Write *add,*
subtract, multiply, or *divide.* Then solve.

1. Mrs. Shaw buys 6 packages of muffins. There are 4 muffins in each package. How many muffins does she buy?

   multiply;

   24 muffins

2. Louisa bakes 12 small cookies and 9 large cookies. How many cookies does she bake in all?

   add;

   21 cookies

3. Mr. Mason uses 20 apples to make pies. He uses 5 apples in each pie. How many pies does he make?

   divide;

   4 pies

4. A large pizza costs $9.00, and a small pizza costs $5.25. How much more does the large pizza cost than the small one?

   subtract;

   $3.75

Harcourt Brace School Publishers

Name _____

LESSON 15.1

Collecting and Organizing Data

Information about people or things is called **data.** Data can be collected and organized in different ways.

Tally Table

A **tally table** uses tally marks to show how often something happens. This table matches the kinds of pants each person is wearing.

Kinds of Pants	
Dark	///
Striped	##// /
Light	//

Frequency Table

A **frequency table** uses numbers to show how often something happens. This table matches the number of people in the picture.

Kinds of Pants	
Dark	3
Striped	6
Light	2

Remember, tally marks are grouped by fives.

Complete the tally table and the frequency table for the picture below.

1.

Kinds of Shirts	
Stripes	## ##
Polka-dots	## //
Flowers	////
Logos	///
Plain	/

2.

Kinds of Shirts	
Stripes	10
Polka-dots	7
Flowers	4
Logos	3
Plain	1

TAKE ANOTHER LOOK   R85

Name _____

Recording Data

An **experiment** is a test done in order to find out something. When a coin is flipped 10 times the results can be recorded in a tally table. Record one tally mark for each flip of a coin.

The picture shows 3 coins with heads on top, and 5 coins with tails on top. Now, look at the tally table. Each time the coin is flipped, the result is recorded with a tally mark. Record the result in a tally table.

COIN-FLIPPING EXPERIMENT	
Side	Tallies
Heads	///
Tails	++++

---

1. Use the picture of flips below to record the tally marks.

Check students' tables.

COIN-FLIPPING EXPERIMENT	
Side	Tallies
Heads	++++
Tails	////

2. Complete the frequency table for the coin-flipping experiment in Problem 1.

3. What side of the coin came up

   the most? _____ **heads** _____

4. Tom did an experiment with a spinner. He spun a 1 five times, a 2 three times, and a 3 seven times. Complete the tally table showing what happened.

COIN-FLIPPING EXPERIMENT	
Side	Frequency
Heads	5
Tails	4

SPINNER EXPERIMENT	
Number	Tallies
1	++++
2	///
3	++++ //

Problem-Solving Strategy

Make a Table

Sam and Matilda are doing an experiment
with two spinners. They will spin each
pointer 20 times to find the sum they spin
the most often and the least often. After
spinning each of the two pointers, they will
add the two numbers they spun. They will
need to record the sums. What would be
the best way to organize and record what
happens in their experiment?

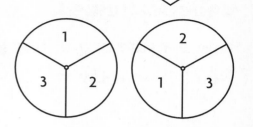

Step 1 Make a table. List all of the
different possible sums.

Step 2 Spin the spinners 20 times each.
Record one tally mark for each sum.

SPINNER EXPERIMENT	
Sum	Number of Times Spun
2	ℋℋ /
3	///
4	///
5	ℋℋ
6	///

Make a table to solve. **Answers will vary. Check students' tables.**

1. Joe and Maria are doing an
experiment with two spinners.
They spin the pointers on the
spinners and then record the
results. They will spin the
pointers 50 times. Show how
they can organize a table
about their experiment.

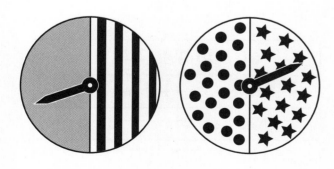

2. Heather is doing an experiment with two spinners. One
spinner has two sections: a
light section and a dark
section. The other spinner
has two sections: A and B.
In the experiment she spins
the pointer and records the
results 50 times. Show how
she could organize a table
about her experiment.

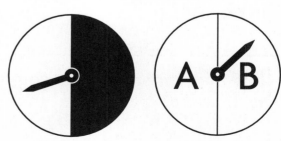

Understanding Collected Data

This is a survey question.

Which is your favorite flavor
of ice cream?
Chocolate
Vanilla
Strawberry

The survey question about ice cream
was asked of 14 people. Their
answers are the results of the survey.

Look at the tally table at the right.
The results of the survey are
recorded using tally marks. It's an
easy way to see what flavors of
ice cream people like best.

Chocolate

Vanilla

Strawberry

OUR FAVORITE ICE-CREAM FLAVORS	
Flavors	**Tallies**
Chocolate	̶H̶H̶ ///
Vanilla	////
Strawberry	//

For Problem 1, use the survey results in the tally table.

1. List the drinks in order from
   the most favorite to the least
   favorite.

   Rooting Root Beer; Paradise

   Punch; Kooky-Kola;

   Strawberry Surprise

OUR FAVORITE DRINKS	
Drink	**Tallies**
Kooky-Kola	///
Strawberry Surprise	//
Rooting Root Beer	̶H̶H̶ ///
Paradise Punch	̶H̶H̶

For Problems 2–3, use the frequency table.

2. How many people were
   surveyed?

   59 people

3. How many more people voted
   yes than *no*?

   5 people

DO YOU OWN A PET?	
Answer	**Number of People**
Yes	32
No	27

Harcourt Brace School Publishers

Grouping Data in a Table

Data can be grouped in different ways. Look at the fish at the right.

Fish can be grouped by size, shape, number of fins, the patterns on their bodies, and so on.

The chart at the right has the fish grouped by size and patterns.

FISH			
	Dots and Stripes	Stripes	Dots
Large	1	2	1
Small	2	4	1

For Problems 1–6, use the table above.

1. How many of the fish have dots only?

     2 fish have dots only.

2. How many large fish are there?

     4 large fish

3. How many small fish have stripes only?

4 small fish have stripes only.

4. How many small fish are there?

     7 small fish

5. How many of the fish have stripes only?

     6 fish have stripes only.

6. How many fish are there in all?

     11 fish

7. In Rebecca's class there are 12 girls and 15 boys. Of the girls, 8 have long hair, 3 have medium-length hair, and the rest have short hair. Of the boys, 2 have long hair, 4 have medium-length hair, and the rest have short hair. Make a table to group the students in the class. **Check students' tables.**

CLASS			
	Long Hair	Medium Hair	Short Hair
Boys	2	4	9
Girls	8	3	1

Reading Pictographs

A **pictograph** shows data by using pictures that stand for more than one thing.

The **key** at the bottom of the pictograph tells how many each picture stands for.

How many students like math best?

Our Favorite Subject	
Math	📖 📖 📖 📖 📖
Reading	📖 📖 📖 📖 📖 📖
History	📖 📖
Science	📖 📖 📖

Key: Each 📖 stands for 2 students.

• Find the subject Math on the pictograph.

• Count how many books are after the name Math.
There are 5 books.

• Read the key below the graph.
Each book stands for 2 students who like that subject best.

• Multiply. $5 \times 2 = 10$
So, 10 students like math best.

---

1. Find how many students like each subject best.
   a. Reading   **b.** History   **c.** Science

   $6 \times 2 = 12$; $2 \times 2 = 4$; $3 \times 2 = 6$;

   12 students   4 students   6 students

2. Which is the favorite subject of the most students? of the fewest students?

   reading; history

3. How many more students like reading best than like history best?

   8 students

4. How many students were in the survey?

   32 students in all

Harcourt Brace School Publishers

Making a Pictograph

A pictograph uses pictures to show information. Use the data from this frequency table to make a pictograph.

- Draw a chart. Title the pictograph.
- Label column 1 "Kind of Pet."
- Label column 2 "Number of Students."
- List the kind of pet in the first column.
- Make a key that shows that each picture equals 2 students.
- Draw pictures to show the number of students for each row.

FAVORITE PETS	
Kind of Pet	**Number of Students**
Dog	16
Cat	10

FAVORITE PETS	
Kind of Pet	**Number of Students**
Dog	☺☺☺☺☺☺☺☺
Cat	☺☺☺☺☺

Key: Each ☺ equals 2 students.

Find Dog on the frequency table. Locate the number after the name. The key says each symbol equals 2 students. So, $16 \div 2 = 8$ pictures.

Make a pictograph that shows the data from the frequency table below. The key should show that each picture stands for 5 students. Check students' pictographs.

FAVORITE DR. SEUSS STORY	
Story	**Number of Votes**
Green Eggs and Ham	25
Hop on Pop	15
The Foot Book	20

FAVORITE DR. SEUSS STORY	
Story	**Number of Votes**
Green Eggs and Ham	📖📖📖📖📖
Hop on Pop	📖📖📖
The Foot Book	📖📖📖📖
Key: Each 📖 equals 5 students.	

Reading Bar Graphs

A **bar graph** uses bars to stand for data. In a **vertical** bar graph, the bars go up. In a **horizontal** bar graph, the bars go across from left to right.

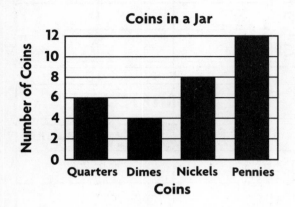

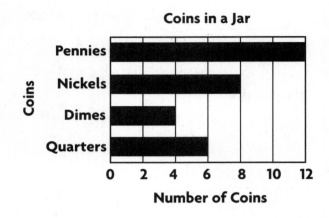

Reading a Vertical Bar Graph
- The title is on top.
- Each bar stands for something.
- Run your finger to the top of a bar.
- Read the number to the left of the top of the bar to see how many.
- The numbers on the left show the amounts of the items.

Reading a Horizontal Bar Graph
- The title is on top.
- Each bar stands for something.
- Run your finger to the far right of a bar.
- Read the number below the end of the bar to see how many.
- The numbers on the bottom show the amounts of the items.

1. Find the number of nickels in the jar. _____ 8 nickels

2. Which coin is there the most of? the fewest of? How can you tell?

   _____ Pennies: the bar is either the highest or the longest; dimes:

   _____ the bar is either the lowest or the shortest.

3. Find the number of pennies in the jar. _____ 12 pennies

Making Bar Graphs

Make a horizontal bar graph of
the data in the frequency table.

- Use the same title.

- Draw a horizontal line and
  mark it off from 0 to 12.

- Draw a vertical line straight
  up from 0.

- Divide this line into
  four equal parts.

- Label each part with
  the names of the meals.

- Make a bar for each meal
  as long as the number of
  votes.

OUR FAVORITE MEAL

Meal	Votes
Breakfast	6
Snack	4
Lunch	10
Dinner	2

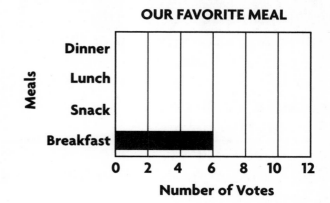

OUR FAVORITE MEAL

For Exercises 1–4, use the data in the frequency table.

1. How long will the bar for
snack be? Draw it.

_____ 4 units long _____

2. How long will the bar for
lunch be? Draw it.

_____ 10 units long _____

3. How long will the bar for
dinner be? Draw it.

_____ 2 units long _____

4. Which bar is 6 units long?

_____ the bar for breakfast _____

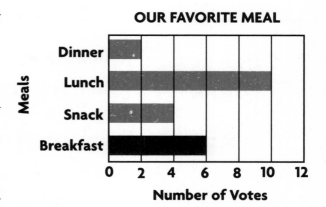

OUR FAVORITE MEAL

Comparing Data

Mr. Thompson's class made this vertical bar graph. It shows information about their favorite places to visit.

Each vertical bar stands for a place Mr. Thompson's class likes to visit.

The numbers on the left stand for the number of students that voted for each place.

You can find how many students liked lakes. Go to the top of the bar for lakes. Read the number to the left. So, 10 students voted for lakes.

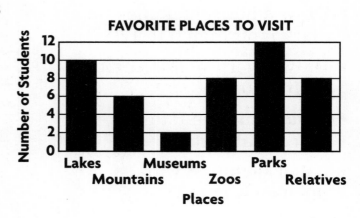

For Exercises 1–4, use the vertical bar graph from Mr. Thompson's class.

1. How many students voted for each place listed?

   a. Mountains   **b.** Museums   **c.** Zoos

      6 students   _2 students_   _8 students_

   d. Parks   **e.** Relatives

      12 students   _8 students_

2. What was the most popular place to visit? Explain.

              Parks; it has the tallest bar.

3. What was the least popular place to visit? Explain.

              Museums; it has the shortest bar.

4. How many more students voted for lakes than for mountains?

              4 more students

Problem-Solving Strategy

Use a Graph

You have taken a survey to find out what number from 1 to 5 the students in your school like most. You made a graph to show the data. Now you need to list the numbers from the least favorite to the most favorite.

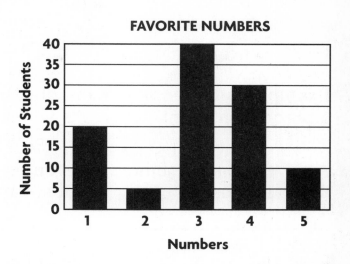

You can create a bar graph like this one to solve the problem.

The least favorite is the shortest bar. So, the number 2 is the least favorite. Compare the other bars and order them from least to most favorite. They are: 2, 5, 1, 4, 3.

For Exercises 1–6, complete the graph and solve.

1. What title would you give the graph?

   Favorite Shapes

2. What label would you put on the side?

   Number of Students

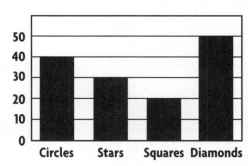

3. What label would you put on the bottom?

   Shapes

4. Which shape was liked the most? the least?

   diamonds; squares

5. How many students voted for stars?

   30 students

6. How many more students voted for circles than for squares?

   20 more students

Certain and Impossible

Example 1. Ordering a pizza is an event.

Example 2. Ice cream melts when it gets hot. That is certain.

Example 3. You will see an elephant fly. That is impossible.

An **event** is something that happens.

An event is **certain** if it will always happen.

An event is **impossible** if it will never happen.

Read each event. Write *certain* or *impossible*.

1. When food comes out of the hot oven, it is hot.

   _____certain_____

2. You can walk on the ocean water.

   _____impossible_____

3. It is cold out when it snows.

   _____certain_____

4. Thanksgiving is celebrated in November.

   _____certain_____

5. You can swim on the grass.

   _____impossible_____

6. You ice skate on ice.

   _____certain_____

7. You will pick a blue ball from a bag filled with yellow and orange balls.

   _____impossible_____

8. If you stand out in the rain without an umbrella, you will get wet.

   _____certain_____

9. Humans can fly like birds.

   _____impossible_____

10. The earth is round.

   _____certain_____

11. The dog will need water.

   _____certain_____

12. Ice cubes will melt in the freezer.

   _____impossible_____

Harcourt Brace School Publishers

Name _____

Recording Possible Outcomes

Example 1

A **possible outcome** is something that has a chance of happening.

Mark enters a contest. He has a chance of winning.

Example 2

An event is **most likely** to happen if it has a greater chance of happening than other events.

Taking an apple is most likely.

Example 3

An event is **least likely** to happen if it has a lesser chance of happening compared to other events.

Picking a number 1 from the bag.

Tell what is *most likely* to happen.

1. tossing a marker on this number line

landing on a 1

2. tossing a bean bag on the gameboard

landing on a happy face

Tell what is *least likely* to happen.

3. spinning the pointer on this spinner

spinning 1

4. spinning the pointer on this spinner

spinning O

Harcourt Brace School Publishers

TAKE ANOTHER LOOK   R97

Problem-Solving Strategy

Make a List

Making a list can help you find the possible outcome of what the students might have for lunch.

Michelle and Tony have two bags. One bag has milk and juice in it. The other bag has a cheese sandwich and a peanut butter sandwich in it. What possible combinations of drinks and sandwiches can they pull from the bags for lunch?

POSSIBLE COMBINATIONS	
Sandwich	Drink
Cheese sandwich	Milk
Cheese sandwich	Juice
Peanut butter sandwich	Milk
Peanut butter sandwich	Juice

You can make a list to help organize the possible results. The list shows you the possible combinations of sandwiches and drinks that the students might have.

Make a list to solve. Check students' lists.

Michelle and Tony now have 3 bags. In bag #1 there are a cheese sandwich and a peanut butter sandwich. In bag #2 there are milk and juice. In bag #3 there are an apple and an orange.

Organize a list of possible combinations of sandwiches, fruit, and drinks the students might have for lunch.

LIST OF POSSIBLE COMBINATIONS		
Sandwich	Drink	Fruit
cheese	milk	apple
cheese	milk	orange
cheese	juice	apple
cheese	juice	orange
peanut butter	milk	apple
peanut butter	milk	orange
peanut butter	juice	apple
peanut butter	juice	orange

1. What information are you trying to find?

   <u>possible combinations of food</u>

   <u>and drinks</u>

2. How many different combinations are there?

   _____8_____

Harcourt Brace School Publishers

Recording Results of an Experiment

When you try an experiment, recording the results in a tally table helps you organize the information.

CUBE ROLL EXPERIMENT

Juan rolls the number cube 6 times.

- Record the results

Use one tally mark to show each result.

- Read the results

Look at the tally table. A 3 is rolled three times, a 1 is rolled two times, and a 4 is rolled one time.

CUBE ROLL EXPERIMENT	
Number Rolled	Tally
1	//
3	///
4	/

For Exercises 1–4, read the following experiment.

Anita and Kim put 30 stickers in a bag. There were heart, star, and clown stickers. Anita and Kim pulled 15 stickers out of the bag. Look at the tally table to see the results.

1. Which sticker was pulled the most?

   _____ star _____

2. Which sticker was pulled the least?

   _____ clown _____

STICKER EXPERIMENT	
Sticker	Tally
Heart	////
Clown	//
Star	‖‖ ////

3. Why do you think one sticker was pulled more than the others?

   _____ Possible answer: There are more star stickers. _____

4. Do you think the results would be different if they did the experiment again?

   _____ Possible answer: Similar numbers would be drawn _____

   _____ reflecting the numbers of stickers in the bag. _____

Fair or Unfair Games

You can decide if a spinner is fair or unfair.

Example 1

- Tusu spins the pointer to see where he should go on the game board.

- Tusu has the same chance of pointing to each color because the sections are the same size and there are the same number of sections.

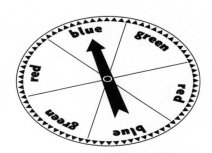

Example 2

- Sheila spins the pointer to see where she should go on the game board.

- Sheila does not have the same chance of pointing to each color because the blue sections are larger than any other color.

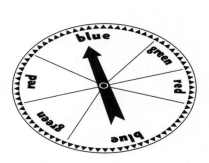

When you play a game, it is fair if you all have an equal chance at winning.

Tell which item is fair. Write *A* or *B*.

1. 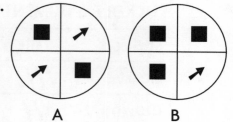 _A_

   A   B

2. 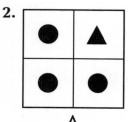 _B_

   A   B

3. 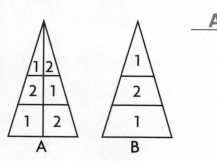 _A_

   A   B

4. 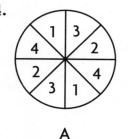 _A_

   A   B

5. What makes the items fair?

Answers will vary.

Harcourt Brace School Publishers

Name _____

Sorting and Comparing Solids

These figures are called solid figures. A flat surface on a solid figure is called a **face.** A straight line where 2 faces meet is called an **edge.** A place where 2 or more edges meet is called a **corner.**

 rectangular prism
 cube
 square pyramid
 sphere
 cone
 cylinder

Write which solid figure each object looks like. Color figures with 6 faces blue. Color figures with 0 edges red. Color figures with only 5 corners green.

1.
(red)
cylinder

2.
(red)
sphere

3.
(blue)
rectangular prism

4.
(green)
square pyramid

5.
(red)
cone

6.
(red)
sphere

7.
(blue)
cube

8.
(red)
cone

9.
(blue)
rectangular prism

10.
(red)
cylinder

11.
(blue)
cube

12.
(green)
square pyramid

Tracing and Naming Faces

A **face** is a flat surface of a solid figure.

A cube has 6 faces.

Each of the faces is a square.

1. How many faces does a square pyramid have? __5__

   How many of the faces are triangles? __4__

   How many of the faces are squares? __1__

2. Each of the objects shown below has the shape of a
   rectangular prism.

   stick of butter   box of crayons   brick

   How many faces does each object have? __6__

3. Name 3 other objects that are shaped like a
   rectangular prism.

   _____ **Answers will vary. Check students' answers.** _____

Circle the word or number that correctly completes
each statement.

4. A rectangular prism has (three)/four pairs of matching faces.

5. A square pyramid has more/(fewer) faces than a cube has.

6. All four/(six) faces of a cube are squares.

7. Five/(four) of the faces on a square pyramid are alike.

8. All faces on a (cube)/rectangular prism are squares.

9. (None)/Some of the faces of a rectangular prism can be triangles.

Harcourt Brace School Publishers

Name _____

Matching Faces to Solids

A **face** is a flat surface of a solid figure.

Each of these solid figures has at least 1 face.

rectangular prism   cube   square pyramid   cone   cylinder

Write the name of the solid figure that has each set of faces.

1. △ △ △ △ ▢ _____square pyramid_____

2.    _____rectangular prism_____

3. ▢ ▢ ▢ ▢ ▢ ▢ _____cube_____

Write the name of the solid figure that answers each riddle.
Choose one of the figures shown at the top of the page.

4. I am a solid figure with 2 faces that are circles.

_____cylinder_____

5. I am a solid figure with 3 pairs of matching faces.

_____rectangular prism_____

6. I am a solid figure with 6 faces that are all the same.

_____cube_____

7. I am a solid figure with only 1 face.

_____cone_____

8. I am a solid figure with 5 faces. Only 1 of my faces is a square.

_____square pyramid_____

9. I have the same number of faces as a cube, but I am not a cube.

_____rectangular prism_____

Plane Figures

A **plane** is a flat surface. You can see parts of planes all around you: a piece of paper, a wall, the floor, and so on.

A **plane figure** is a closed figure in a plane. A plane figure is flat. It does not have 3 dimensions as a solid figure does.

A plane figure is formed by lines that are curved, straight, or both.

curved lines   straight lines   both curved and straight lines

---

Tell whether each figure is formed by only straight lines, only curved lines, or both straight and curved lines. Write *straight, curved,* or *both.*

1.   2.    3.   4.

   __curved__   __both__   __curved__   __straight__

5.   6. 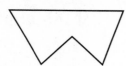   7.   8.

   __both__   __straight__   __straight__   __curved__

Draw a closed plane figure in each box.
Students' drawings will vary. Check students' drawings.

9.	10.	11.
straight lines	curved lines	straight and curved lines

Harcourt Brace School Publishers

Patterns with Plane Figures

John made a pattern using squares and circles. He repeated the pattern 3 times.

Mary made a pattern using diamonds, circles, and triangles. She repeated the pattern 2 times.

Draw a circle around the pattern that repeats. Then write the number of times the pattern repeats.

Number of Repetitions

1. ⬡ △ ⬡ △ ⬡ △ ⬡ △ ⬡ △   4

2. △ ▯ ○ △ ▯ ○ △ ▯ ○ △ ▯ ○   3

3. ◇ △ ◇ ○ ◇ △ ◇ ○ ◇ △ ◇ ○   2

4. ⧖ ○ ○ ⧖ ○ ○ ⧖ ○ ○ ⧖ ○ ○   4

5. △ ▽ △ △ ▽ △ △ ▽ △   2

Tell the missing shapes in each pattern.

6. △ □ ○ _ △ _ ○ ○ △ □ _ ○

_____circle, square, circle_____

7. _ ◇ _ □ ○ _ ◇ □ ○ ◇ ◇ □

_____circle, diamond, diamond_____

TAKE ANOTHER LOOK   R105

Problem-Solving Strategy

Find a Pattern

What shapes come next?

Look for the place where the pattern repeats.

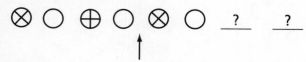

The next shapes are: ⊕ ○

What shapes are missing?

Identify the repeating pattern.

The missing shapes are: ✕ and ☐

Draw a circle around the pattern that repeats. Then draw
the shapes that are missing.

1.

2. ⊓ ∨ ∨ ⊓ ∨ ∨ ⊓ ∨ ∨

3. ○ ☐ ◇ ○ ☐ ◇ ○ ☐ ◇

4. △ ○ ○ ☐ △ ○ ○ ☐ △ ○ ○ ☐

5. ⌂ ☐ △ ⌂ ☐ △ ⌂ ☐ △

6.  A B A C A B A C A B A C

Harcourt Brace School Publishers

Name _____

Line Segments and Angles

A **line segment** is straight.

An **angle** is formed where two line segments cross or meet.
The number of angles equals the number of line segments.

A square has
4 line segments.

A circle has no
line segments.

A triangle has
3 line segments.

 4 angles

0 angles

 3 angles

For each figure below, write the number of line segments
and the number of angles. Circle the angles.

1.
Yellow

line segments __4__

angles __4__

2.
Yellow

line segments __4__

angles __4__

3.
Blue

line segments __0__

angles __0__

4.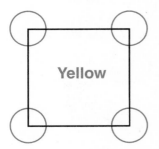
Yellow

line segments __4__

angles __4__

5.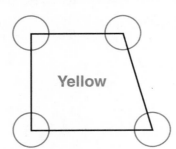
Yellow

line segments __4__

angles __4__

6.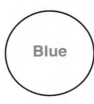
Red

line segments __3__

angles __3__

7. Color all the figures with 3 line segments red.

8. Color all the figures with 0 line segments blue.

9. Color all the figures with 4 line segments yellow.

Harcourt Brace School Publishers

Locating Points on a Grid

An ordered pair of numbers helps you find places on a grid. The numbers tell you how many places to move to the right of zero and how many to move up.

Locate the baseball on the grid.

1. Start at zero and move two spaces to the right.

2. From that point, move up three spaces.

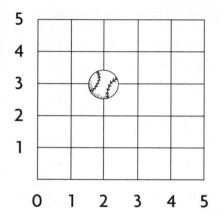

Look at the ordered pairs of numbers. Name the sporting equipment you find at each point.

1. (3,1) ___tennis ball___

2. (1,2) ___baseball bat___

3. (4,4) ___basketball___

4. (5,6) ___tennis racket___

5. (6,2) ___football___

6. (2,3) ___hockey stick___

7. (7,5) ___soccer ball___

8. (1,6) ___volley ball___

9. (5,1) ___baseball glove___

10. (2,5) ___sneakers___

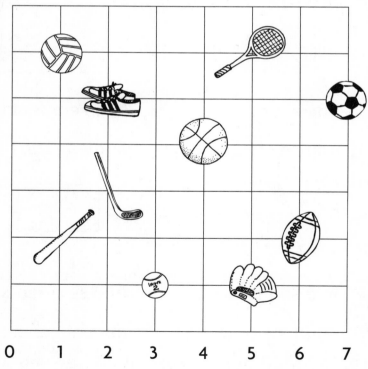

Congruent Figures

Congruent figures have the same *size* and *shape*.

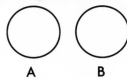

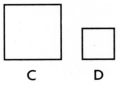

- Trace and cut out circle B.

- Place circle B over circle A.

The figures are the same size and shape.

So, circle A and circle B are congruent.

- Trace and cut out square D.

- Place square D over square C.

The figures are the same shape but not the same size.

So, square C and square D are not congruent.

Trace figure B. Place over figure A. Write *yes* or *no* to tell if the shapes are congruent.

1.

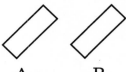

__yes__

2.

__no__

3.

__yes__

4.

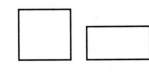

__no__

5.

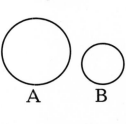

__no__

6.

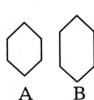

__no__

Using Congruent Figures

You can make interesting designs using congruent figures. Two figures are congruent when they are the same size and shape. Figures are congruent even when they are turned around into another position.

| 1 | 2 / 3 | 4 / 5 | 6 / 7 | 8 | 9 / 10 | 11 / 12 |

Figures 1 and 8 are congruent.

Figures 2, 3, 9, and 10 are congruent.

Figures 4, 5, 11, and 12 are congruent.

Figures 6 and 7 are congruent.

Look at the design below. Find the number of figures that are congruent to the figures A through D. Record your findings in the table.

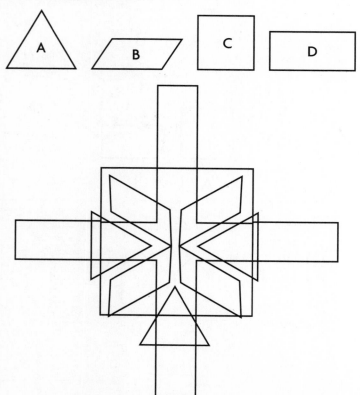

Figure	Number of Congruent Figures
A	3
B	4
C	4
D	4

Harcourt Brace School Publishers

Name _____

Congruent Solid Figures

Cubes are called solid shapes. Cubes have 6 sides, and the sides are equal length.

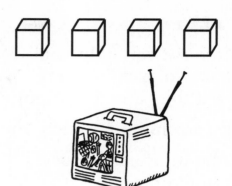

A lot of the shapes we see daily are made from solid cubes.

The TV is a cube because it has 6 sides and the sides are equal length.

Below are pictures of items we see in our daily lives. Write *yes* or *no* to tell if the shape is a cube.

1.

   Yes

2.

   Yes

3.

   No

4.

   Yes

5.

   No

6.

   Yes

7.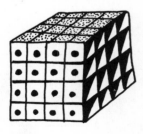

   Yes

8.

   No

9.

   Yes

Harcourt Brace School Publishers

Problem-Solving Strategy

Make a List

Making a list can help you compare two or more items. You can see if they are congruent.

- Make a column for each building.

- List the information for each building.

- You can anwer the question, "Are the buildings congruent?"

Yes; they have the same number of floors, windows, and antennas.

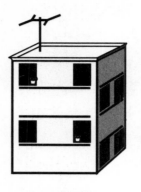
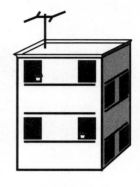

Building A
4 floors
8 windows
1 antenna

Building B
4 floors
8 windows
1 antenna

Complete the lists. Tell whether the buildings are congruent. Write *yes* or *no*. Lists will vary.

Building A   **Building B**

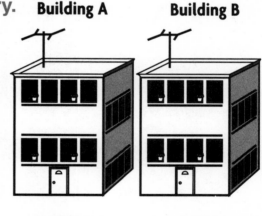

1. Building A   Building B

   __4 floors__   __4 floors__

__16 windows__   __16 windows__

  __1 door__   __1 door__

Are they congruent? __yes__

Building A   **Building B**

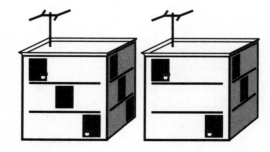

2. Building A   Building B

  __3 floors__   __3 floors__

 __6 windows__   __4 windows__

__1 antenna__   __1 antenna__

Are they congruent? __no__

Harcourt Brace School Publishers

Sliding, Flipping, and Turning

An object can be moved in different ways.

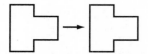      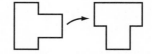

You can **slide** it.   You can **flip** it.   You can **turn** it.

Draw how each letter would look if you were to slide it,
flip it over the line, or turn it. Check students'
drawings. Turn drawings may vary.

	Slide	Flip	Turn
P	P	q	P
O	O	O	O
M	M	M	M
H	H	H	H
Z	Z	Z	N
N	N	И	Z

Harcourt Brace School Publishers

Symmetry

A **line of symmetry** is an imaginary line that divides a figure in half. If you fold a figure along a line of symmetry, the two sides match.

You can make a figure from your name that has a line of symmetry!

MATERIALS: paper, crayon

Step 1

Fold a sheet of paper lengthwise.

Step 2

Open the paper. Print your name along the folded line. Be sure to press down hard with your crayon to make the print heavy.

Step 3

Cover your name by refolding the paper on the same line. Press down hard along the folded line.

Step 4

Open the paper. What do you see?

1. Where is the line of symmetry on your paper?

_____ **on the fold** _____

2. Is the left half of your figure congruent with the right half? Explain how you know.

_____ **Yes; if you fold the paper so that one half is** _____

_____ **on top of the other, they match.** _____

_____

3. Is each matching letter formed from a slide, a flip, or a turn of the letter you drew?

_____ **a flip** _____

Name ______________________________

LESSON 20.3

More About Symmetry

Some letters and numbers have one or more lines of symmetry.

The letter H has two lines of symmetry.

You can fold this letter two different ways to get matching sides.

H H

The letter A has only one line of symmetry.

You can fold this letter only one way to get matching sides.

A

Draw the line or lines of symmetry on each letter or number.

1. E
2. 3
3. U
4. W
5. 8
6. X
7. Y
8. M
9. T

10. Write 2 other capital letters that have only one line of symmetry. **V, B** **Possible answers are given.**
11. Write 3 numbers between 1 and 10 that have no lines of symmetry. **2, 4, 6** **Possible answers are given.**
12. Write 1 other capital letter that has two lines of symmetry. **O** **Possible answer is given.**

Symmetric Patterns

If you place one half of a symmetric figure or pattern against a
mirror along the figure's or pattern's line of symmetry, the reflection
shows the other half. You see the whole figure or pattern.

If you hold this
figure against a
mirror along its
line of symmetry . . .

. . . the reflection
will show the
other half . . .

. . . so you will see
the whole figure.

Look at the first figure in each row. Circle the letter of the
figure that would be reflected in a mirror.

1.
   a   b   **c**

2.
      a   b   c

3.
   a   **b**   c

4.
    a   b   c

5.
    a    **b**   c

Problem-Solving Strategy

Draw a Picture

You can use symmetry to draw a picture.

Syd and Whit are making
a connect-the-dots drawing
on grid paper. Syd drew
the first half. Whit must
draw the other half on
the other side of the line
of symmetry.

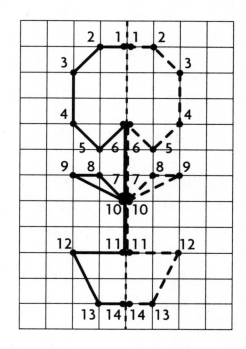

Whit has a plan. He will
mark dots that match
Syd's but go in opposite
directions. Then he will
connect his dots. The two
halves will match to make
a complete drawing.

Use Syd and Whit's plan to
complete the figure. Mark
and number dots on the left
side of the line of symmetry.
Then mark, number, and
connect matching dots on
the other side to complete
your drawing. Check
students' drawings. Dots
and numbers will vary.

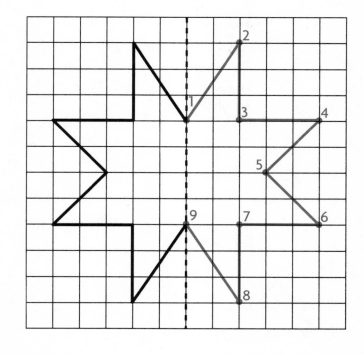

Modeling Parts of a Whole

1. Mel made a flag from 4 cloth squares of the same size. He wants to know how many parts make up the whole.

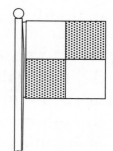

   a. Look at the model of the flag. Count the number of small squares in the flag. How many small

   squares are in the whole flag? ___4___

   b. How many parts make up the whole? ___4___

   c. How many of those parts are shaded? ___2___

2. Nancy folded a piece of paper into equal parts and shaded some of the parts. How many of the parts are shaded?

   a. Look at the model of the piece of paper. Count the number of parts in the whole.

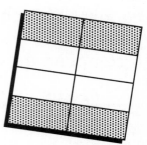

   How many parts make up the whole? ___8___

   b. How many of those parts are shaded? ___4___

   c. How many of those parts are NOT shaded? ___4___

Tell how many parts make up the whole. Then tell how many parts are shaded.

3.

_____2 parts; 1 part_____

4.

_____16 parts; 8 parts_____

5.

_____4 parts; 3 parts_____

6.

_____16 parts; 9 parts_____

Harcourt Brace School Publishers

Other Ways to Model Fractions

A **fraction** is a number that names a part of a whole. The **numerator** tells how many parts are being used. The **denominator** tells how many equal parts are in the whole.

$$\frac{2}{3} \quad \begin{array}{l} \leftarrow \text{Numerator} \\ \leftarrow \text{Denominator} \end{array}$$

A fraction tells about itself. For example, $\frac{3}{4}$ tells you that a whole is divided into 4 equal parts and that 3 of those parts are being used. So, you can draw and shade it:

 or or  or

---

1. Draw and shade $\frac{1}{2}$ in this shape: **Students' shadings will vary.**

2. Draw and shade $\frac{2}{3}$ in this shape: **Students' shadings will vary.**

3. Draw and shade $\frac{2}{4}$ in this shape: **Students' shadings will vary.**

4. Draw and shade $\frac{5}{6}$ in this shape: **Students' shadings will vary.**

5. Brian had a piece of rope. He cut it into 8 equal parts. He used 3 of the parts on a project. What fraction of the rope did Brian use?

   a. How many equal parts make up the rope? _____8_____

   b. How many parts did Brian use? _____3_____

   c. What fraction of the rope did he use? _____$\frac{3}{8}$_____

6. There are 12 cans of juice in a carton. Al and his friends drink 5 of them. What part of the carton did Al and his friends drink?

   a. How many equal parts are in the carton? _____12_____

   b. How many parts were used by Al and his friends? _____5_____

   c. What fraction of the carton did they use? _____$\frac{5}{12}$_____

Counting Parts to Make a Whole

A group of students are making a quilt. Each student is making $\frac{1}{6}$ of the quilt.

Deb	Bill
John	Nate
Elia	Georgia

a. What fractional part of the quilt is Deb making?
Each student is making $\frac{1}{6}$ of the quilt, so Deb is
making $\frac{1}{6}$ of the quilt.

b. What fractional parts of the quilt are Deb, Bill,
and Joe making? Each student is making 1 of 6
equal parts, so 3 students are making 3 of 6
equal parts, or $\frac{3}{6}$.

c. How many parts make up the whole quilt? This
whole quilt is made up of 6 equal parts.

d. How many students are needed to make the whole
quilt? The quilt has 6 equal parts, so 6 students
are needed.

A soccer team is making a banner. Each team
member is making $\frac{1}{12}$ of the banner.

A	B	C	D	E	F
G	H	I	J	K	L

1. What fractional part of the
banner is labeled A? $\frac{1}{12}$

2. What fractional part of the banner is labeled A or B? $\frac{2}{12}$

3. What fractional part of the banner is labeled A, B, C,
D, E, F, G, H, I, J, K, or L? $\frac{12}{12}$

4. What fractional part of the banner is not labeled L? $\frac{11}{12}$

5. How many parts make up the whole banner? 12

6. How many team members are needed to make
the whole banner? 12

Comparing Fractions

Solve. Use fraction bars to help you.

1. Dennis ran $\frac{2}{5}$ of a mile. Rita ran $\frac{4}{5}$ of a mile. Who ran farther?

   a. Look at the fractions. How are they alike?

   _____ same denominator _____

   b. What does this show about the number of equal

   parts in each whole? _____ They are the same. _____

   c. Which fraction has the larger numerator? __$\frac{4}{5}$__

   d. Which fraction tells that a greater number of equal

   parts are used? __$\frac{4}{5}$__

   e. Who ran farther? _____ Rita _____

2. Jon has a piece of wire that is $\frac{1}{2}$ ft long. He also has a piece
   of wire that is $\frac{1}{3}$ ft long. Which piece of wire is longer?

   a. Look at the fractions. What is the numerator of each

   fraction? __1__

   b. Look at the denominators. Are they the same

   number? __no__

   c. A denominator tells how many equal parts are in a whole.
   Which fraction's denominator tells about more equal parts?

   __$\frac{1}{3}$__

   d. What happens to the size of the parts as the denominator

   gets larger? _____ The parts get smaller. _____

   e. So, which fraction tells about a smaller part of 1 foot?

   __$\frac{1}{3}$__

   f. Which piece of wire is longer? _____ $\frac{1}{2}$ ft _____

Problem-Solving Strategy

Draw a Picture

At track practice, 3 team members ran parts of a mile. Tiko ran $\frac{3}{8}$ of a mile. Raoul ran $\frac{2}{3}$ of a mile. Jed ran $\frac{3}{6}$ of a mile. Who ran the farthest?

UNDERSTAND

1. What are you asked to find? _____ Who ran the farthest?

2. How will you do this? _____ by comparing

3. What information will you use? _____ Tiko ran $\frac{3}{8}$ mi; Raoul ran $\frac{2}{3}$ mi; Jed ran $\frac{3}{6}$ mi

PLAN

4. What strategy can you use to solve the problem?

draw a picture

SOLVE

5. How can you draw a picture that will help you compare?

   a. Draw three lines of equal length directly under one another. Each line stands for 1 mile. Label one line "Tiko," one "Raoul," and the other "Jed." Then, mark each boy's distance on his line.

   Check students' drawings.

   b. Now you can compare distances.

6. Who ran the farthest? _____ Raoul

Harcourt Brace School Publishers

Equivalent Fractions

Equivalent fractions are two or more fractions that name the same amount.

The following will help you make a model of some equivalent fractions.

    a. Cut pieces of string that are each 8 inches long.

    b. Tape one string lengthwise on a piece of paper. This will be your model for one whole, or $\frac{1}{1}$.

    c. Cut the second string in half. Tape the 2 pieces end-to-end next to the first string. Each piece will be your model for $\frac{1}{2}$.

Notice that $\frac{2}{2} = \frac{1}{1}$.

    d. Cut the third string into 4 equal parts. Tape the 4 pieces end-to-end next to the second string. Each piece will be your model for $\frac{1}{4}$.

Notice that $\frac{4}{4} = \frac{2}{2} = \frac{1}{1}$.

    e. Cut the fourth string into 8 equal parts. Tape the 8 pieces end-to-end next to the third string. Each piece will be your model for $\frac{1}{8}$.

Notice these equivalent fractions: $\frac{8}{8} = \frac{4}{4} = \frac{2}{2} = \frac{1}{1}$.

Find an equivalent fraction for each. Use your model to help you.

1. $\frac{1}{4} = \frac{\boxed{2}}{8}$ 2. $\frac{2}{2} = \frac{\boxed{8}}{8}$ 3. $\frac{3}{4} = \frac{\boxed{6}}{8}$

4. $\frac{1}{2} = \frac{\boxed{2}}{4}$ 5. $\frac{1}{1} = \frac{\boxed{8}}{8}$ 6. $\frac{2}{4} = \frac{\boxed{4}}{8}$

7. $\frac{1}{2} = \frac{\boxed{4}}{8}$ 8. $\frac{2}{2} = \frac{\boxed{4}}{4}$ 9. $\frac{4}{4} = \frac{\boxed{8}}{8}$

Name _____

Part of a Group

2 marbles
1 marble is shaded

4 marbles
2 equal parts
1 part is shaded

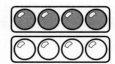

8 marbles
2 equal parts
1 part is shaded

Each of the pictures shows 2 equal parts with 1 part shaded.

Look at the picture. Then fill in the blanks.

1.

1 part shaded

__3__ parts not shaded

__4__ equal parts

2.

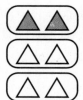

1 part shaded

__2__ parts not shaded

__3__ equal parts

3.

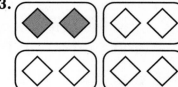

1 part shaded

__3__ parts not shaded

__4__ equal parts

Circle the parts that are equal to the shaded part. Then fill in the blank.

4.

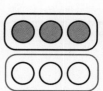

1 part shaded

__2__ equal parts

5.

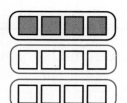

1 part shaded

__3__ equal parts

6.

2 parts shaded

__5__ equal parts

Fractions of a Group

You can use fractions to tell about part of a group.

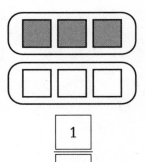

numerator | 1 | number of shaded parts
denominator | 3 | total number of parts

Complete each fraction to tell about the part that is shaded.

1.

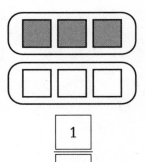

$\dfrac{1}{2}$

2.

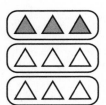

$\dfrac{1}{3}$

3.

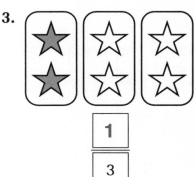

$\dfrac{1}{3}$

4.

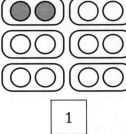

$\dfrac{1}{6}$

5.

$\dfrac{1}{6}$

6.

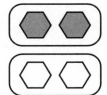

$\dfrac{1}{2}$

7.

$\dfrac{1}{4}$

8.

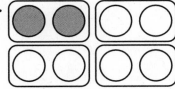

$\dfrac{1}{4}$

9.

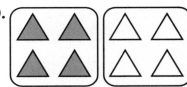

$\dfrac{1}{2}$

More About Fractions of a Group

You can use fractions to describe more than one part of a group.

| **numerator** | 3 | number of shaded blocks |
| **denominator** | 4 | total number of blocks |

Write the fraction for the part that is shaded.

1.

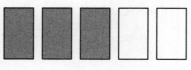

$$\frac{3}{5}$$

2.

$$\frac{2}{7}$$

3.

$$\frac{7}{8}$$

4.

$$\frac{1}{6}$$

5.

$$\frac{1}{2}$$

6.

$$\frac{2}{8}$$ or $$\frac{1}{4}$$

7.

$$\frac{3}{6}$$ or $$\frac{1}{2}$$

8.

$$\frac{2}{3}$$

9.

$$\frac{2}{6}$$ or $$\frac{1}{3}$$

Problem-Solving Strategy

Draw a Picture

Jeff has 12 marbles. There are 3 black marbles. What fraction of the marbles are black?

Draw 12 marbles.

Color 3 marbles black.

Draw rings around groups of 3.

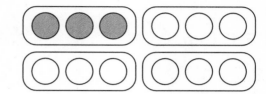

There are 4 groups of 3 in 12.

So, $\frac{1}{4}$ of the marbles are black.

Check students' drawings.
Draw a picture to the right of each problem to solve.

1. There are 12 cars in the parking lot, and 2 of the cars are blue. What fraction of the cars are blue?

   $\frac{1}{6}$ **of the cars**

2. Mrs. Lopez baked 12 cookies. She put 4 cookies in each bag. What fraction of the cookies did she put in each bag? How many bags did she use?

   $\frac{1}{3}$ **of the cookies; 3 bags**

3. Lisa and Jack shared a set of 12 markers equally. How many markers did each person get? What fraction of the set of markers did each person get?

   6 markers; $\frac{1}{2}$ **of the set**

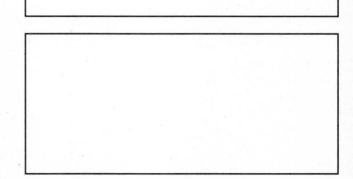

Name _____

Comparing Parts of a Group

Compare $\frac{1}{3}$ and $\frac{2}{3}$.

$\frac{1}{3}$ is less than $\frac{2}{3}$.

$$\frac{1}{3} < \frac{2}{3}$$

Compare $\frac{3}{4}$ and $\frac{1}{4}$.

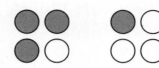

$\frac{3}{4}$ is greater than $\frac{1}{4}$.

$$\frac{3}{4} > \frac{1}{4}$$

Compare. Write $<$, $>$, or $=$ in the ◯.
Remember to point the arrow to the smaller fraction.

1.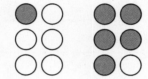

$\frac{1}{6}$ ⦗$<$⦘ $\frac{5}{6}$

2.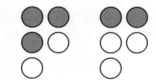

$\frac{3}{5}$ ⦗$>$⦘ $\frac{2}{5}$

3.

$\frac{3}{8}$ ⦗$<$⦘ $\frac{5}{8}$

4.

$\frac{4}{7}$ ⦗$=$⦘ $\frac{4}{7}$

5.

$\frac{1}{2}$ ⦗$>$⦘ $\frac{1}{3}$

6.

$\frac{1}{4}$ ⦗$<$⦘ $\frac{1}{2}$

7.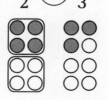

$\frac{1}{2}$ ⦗$>$⦘ $\frac{3}{8}$

8.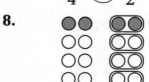

$\frac{2}{8}$ ⦗$=$⦘ $\frac{1}{4}$

Tenths

A **decimal** is a number that uses place value and a decimal point to show amounts that are less than one. One amount less than one that decimals can show is the fraction **tenths**.

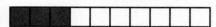

Three out of the bar's 10 squares are shaded. Three tenths are shaded.

Three tenths can be written as a fraction: $\frac{3}{10}$

Three tenths can also be written as a decimal:

Ones	Tenths
0	3

↑
decimal point

Write a fraction and a decimal to show what part of each bar is shaded.

		Fraction	Decimal

1. $\frac{6}{10}$ 0.6

2. $\frac{8}{10}$ 0.8

3. $\frac{9}{10}$ 0.9

4. $\frac{2}{10}$ 0.2

Draw lines to match each bar with an equivalent fraction and decimal.

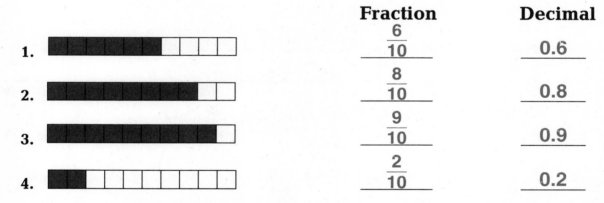

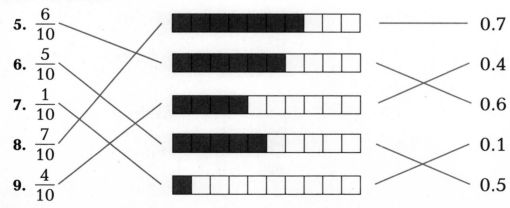

5. $\frac{6}{10}$

6. $\frac{5}{10}$

7. $\frac{1}{10}$

8. $\frac{7}{10}$

9. $\frac{4}{10}$

0.7

0.4

0.6

0.1

0.5

Hundredths

A decimal is a number that uses place value and a decimal point to show amounts that are less than one. One amount less than one that decimals can show is the fraction **hundredths.**

Six parts out of the decimal square's 100 equal parts are shaded.
Six hundredths are shaded.

Write as a fraction: $\dfrac{6}{100}$

Write as a decimal:

Ones	Tenths	Hundredths
0	0	6

Twenty-six parts out of the decimal square's 100 equal parts are shaded.
Twenty-six hundredths are shaded.

Write as a fraction: $\dfrac{26}{100}$

Write as a decimal:

Ones	Tenths	Hundredths
0	2	6

Write a fraction and a decimal to show what part of each decimal square is shaded.

1. 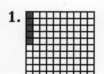   Fraction: $\dfrac{5}{100}$

   Decimal: __0.05__

2.   Fraction: $\dfrac{35}{100}$

   Decimal: __0.35__

3.   Fraction: $\dfrac{47}{100}$

   Decimal: __0.47__

4.   Fraction: $\dfrac{52}{100}$

   Decimal: __0.52__

5.   Fraction: $\dfrac{4}{100}$

   Decimal: __0.04__

6.   Fraction: $\dfrac{40}{100}$

   Decimal: __0.40__

Name _____

Reading and Writing Hundredths

You can write a fraction or a decimal to tell how many
parts out of 100 are shaded. Both are read the same way.

Model	Fraction	Decimal	Read
	$\frac{25}{100}$	0.25	twenty-five hundredths

Complete the table.

	Model	Fraction	Decimal	Read
1.		$\frac{44}{100}$	0.44	forty-four hundredths
2.		$\frac{15}{100}$	0.15	fifteen hundredths
3.		$\frac{2}{100}$	0.02	two hundredths

Shade the model to show each amount. **Check students' models.**

4. thirty-six hundredths

5. 0.14

6. $\frac{25}{100}$

7. ninety-eight hundredths

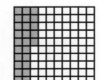

Decimals Greater Than 1

A mixed number with a fractional part of tenths or hundredths can be written as a whole number and a decimal. A whole number with a decimal is called a **mixed decimal**. A decimal point separates the whole number part from the fractional part of a number. We read the decimal point as "and."

2 wholes + 3 tenths, or $2\frac{3}{10}$,

1 whole + 45 hundredths, or $1\frac{45}{100}$,

or
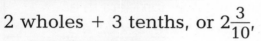

Ones	Tenths
2	3

or

Ones	Tenths	Hundredths
1	4	5

Read: two and three tenths

Read: one and forty-five hundredths

Write a mixed number and then a mixed decimal for the shaded amounts. Then write how the mixed number and decimal are read.

1.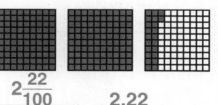

$2\frac{22}{100}$ _____ 2.22 _____

two and twenty-two

hundredths

2.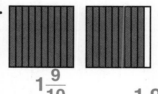

$1\frac{9}{10}$ _____ 1.9 _____

one and nine tenths

3.

$1\frac{10}{100}$ _____ 1.10 _____

one and ten hundredths

4.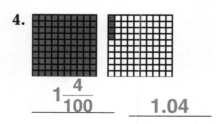

$1\frac{4}{100}$ _____ 1.04 _____

one and four hundredths

Write each number as a decimal.

5. two and five tenths __2.5__

6. three and two hundredths __3.02__

Comparing Decimal Numbers

Compare decimal numbers by their place values.

2.3   (?)   2.1

Compare the whole numbers.   **Then compare the tenths.**

Ones	Tenths
2	3
2	1

2 = 2   3 > 1

Begin with the place value farther to the left. Then move to the right, comparing the numbers in each place value. Here, because 3 is greater than 1, the number 2.3 is greater than 2.1.

So, 2.3 > 2.1

Compare the decimals by their place values. Write < or > in the ◯. For Exercises 1–2, use the table to the right to help you.

1.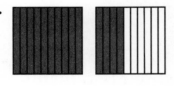

Ones	Tenths
1	4
1	7

1.4 (<) 1.7

1 = 1   4 < 7

2.

Ones	Tenths
2	1
1	9

2.1 (>) 1.9

2 > 1 no need to compare

3. 2.5 (<) 2.7   **4.** 0.3 (>) 0.1   **5.** 1.9 (<) 2.1

6. 7.2 (>) 2.7   **7.** 5.5 (>) 5.0   **8.** 0.4 (<) 0.8

9. 4.0 (<) 4.1   **10.** 0.6 (<) 6.0   **11.** 3.6 (>) 3.2

Problem-Solving Strategy

Draw a picture

Joanna walks 0.2 mile to school. Brad walks 0.5 mile to school. Who walks farther?

You can draw models to compare the distances.

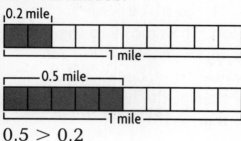

$0.5 > 0.2$

So, Brad walks farther than Joanna.

You can compare the distances on a number line.

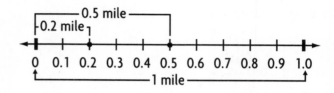

$0.5 > 0.2$

So, Brad walks farther than Joanna.

Solve. You may draw a model or a number line to help you.

1. Ted is 1.4 meters tall. Jeremy is 1.3 meters tall. Who is taller?

    _____ Ted _____

2. Greta ate 0.4 of a pizza. Jane ate 0.3 of the same pizza. Who ate more pizza?

    _____ Greta _____

3. Carla rode her bicycle 3.4 miles on Saturday and 4.1 miles on Sunday. On which day did Carla ride farther?

    _____ Sunday _____

4. Tom measured two plants in his garden. The bean plant is 23.5 centimeters tall. The corn plant is 24.5 centimeters tall. Which plant is taller?

    _____ corn plant _____

5. A math paper has 10 problems. Charles finished $\frac{7}{10}$ of the problems. Tracey finished $\frac{6}{10}$ of the problems. Who finished more problems?

    _____ Charles _____

6. Mrs. Jones lives $\frac{3}{10}$ of a mile from the library. Mr. Davis lives 0.2 mile from the library. Who lives closer to the library?

    _____ Mr. Davis _____

Harcourt Brace School Publishers

Inch, Foot, Yard, and Mile

The **inch (in.)**, **foot (ft)**, **yard (yd)**, and **mile (mi)** are customary units used to measure length or distance.

The length of a grasshopper is about 1 inch.

The length of Mr. Lee's boot is about 1 foot.

The height of Sara's little brother is about 1 yard.

The distance across Clearwater Lake is about 1 mile.

Complete each sentence. Write *more* or *less*.

1. The length of a jump rope is _____**more**_____ than 1 foot.

2. The length of a paintbrush is _____**more**_____ than 1 inch.

3. The distance you can throw a ball is _____**less**_____ than 1 mile.

4. The length of a sunflower seed is _____**less**_____ than 1 inch.

5. The length of a spoon is _____**less**_____ than 1 yard.

6. The height of a goat is _____**more**_____ than 1 foot.

7. The length of a classroom is _____**more**_____ than 1 yard.

8. The distance around a city is _____**more**_____ than 1 mile.

Choose the best unit to measure each item. Match by drawing a line.

9. the height of a door ——————————— inch

10. the distance around a football field ——————— yard

11. the length of a carrot ——————————— mile

12. the distance from Earth to the sun ——————— foot

Estimating and Comparing Length

Sometimes you want to know **about** how long an object is.

You can use a ruler to measure an object to the nearest inch.

- Line up the left edge of the ruler with one end of the object.
- Look at the other end of the object. Find the closest inch mark.

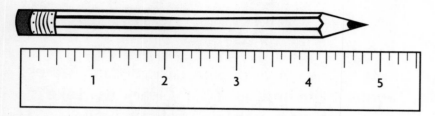

The tip of the pencil is between the 4-inch mark and the 5-inch mark.

It is nearer to the 5-inch mark.

The pencil is about 5 inches long, to the nearest inch.

Estimate the length of each object to the nearest inch.
Then use a ruler to measure to the nearest inch. **Estimates will vary.**

		Estimate	Measure
1.	EXCEL CAN OPENER	_____ in.	3 in.
2.		_____ in.	1 in.
3.		_____ in.	3 in.

Draw a line with your ruler from the | to show the length.

4. 2 inches

5. 4 inches

Harcourt Brace School Publishers

Measuring to the Nearest Half Inch

Sometimes you need a measurement that is more accurate than to the nearest inch. You might measure to the nearest half inch.

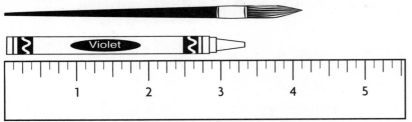

The tip of the crayon is just before the halfway mark between 3 and 4 inches. It is closer to the $3\frac{1}{2}$-inch mark than it is to the 3-inch or the 4-inch mark.

The tip of the paintbrush is just past the 4-inch mark. It is closer to the 4-inch mark than to the $4\frac{1}{2}$-inch mark. The paintbrush is 4 inches, to the nearest half inch.

Use a ruler to measure each object to the nearest half inch.

1.  ____$5\frac{1}{2}$____ in.

2.  ____4____ in.

3.  ____$3\frac{1}{2}$____ in.

4. 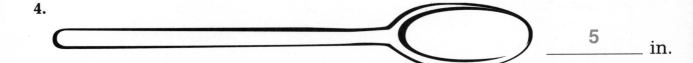 ____5____ in.

Problem-Solving Strategy

Make a Model

Kevin's bean plant is $16\frac{1}{2}$ inches tall. Amanda's bean plant is 12 inches tall. How much taller is Kevin's plant than Amanda's?

You can *make a model* to solve the problem.

Measure the plants, and cut a length of string (or a strip of paper) to match the length of each plant. Line up the ends of the strings. Measure the difference in their lengths.

So, Kevin's plant is $4\frac{1}{2}$ inches taller than Amanda's plant.

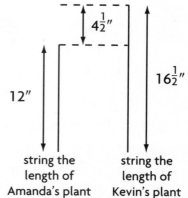

string the length of Amanda's plant   string the length of Kevin's plant

---

Solve. You may *make a model* to help you.

1. Gail's pencil is $7\frac{1}{2}$ inches long. Ben's pencil is 4 inches long. How much longer is Gail's pencil than Ben's?

   $3\frac{1}{2}$ in.

2. Becky has a ribbon that is 25 inches long. She cuts off a 12-inch length of ribbon. How much ribbon is left?

   13 in.

3. Doug has a strip of paper that is 20 inches long and 1 inch wide. He makes bookmarks that are 4 inches long and 1 inch wide. How many bookmarks can he make?

   5 bookmarks

4. A snail is climbing up a short wall that is 13 inches high. The snail has climbed halfway up the wall. How many inches has the snail climbed?

   $6\frac{1}{2}$ in.

5. A photograph that is 5 inches wide and 7 inches long is mounted on a piece of paper. There is a 1-inch border around the photograph. How wide is the paper?

   7 in.

6. A plant grew 2 inches in one week and 3 times that in the next week. How much did the plant grow during the two weeks?

   8 in.

Harcourt Brace School Publishers

Estimating and Comparing Capacity

Capacity is the amount of liquid a container can hold when filled. The **cup (c)**, **pint (pt)**, **quart (qt)**, and **gallon (gal)** are customary units used to measure capacity.

2 cups = 1 pint   2 pints = 1 quart   4 quarts = 1 gallon

Circle the unit of measure that is larger.

1. cup (pint)   2. (gallon) quart   3. (quart) pint

Complete each sentence. Write *more* or *less*.

4. A swimming pool contains ____more____ than 1 gallon.

5. A juice pitcher contains ____more____ than 1 pint.

6. Your cupped hands can contain ____less____ than 1 pint.

7. A coffee mug contains ____less____ than 1 quart.

8. A large thermos contains ____more____ than 1 cup.

Circle the measurement that correctly completes the math sentence. You may use the models above or make your own to help you.

9. 4 quarts = (8 pints)/ 16 pints   10. 1 pint = 4 cups /(2 cups)

11. 1 quart =(4 cups)/ 4 pints   12. 2 gallons = 8 pints /(16 pints)

13. 1 pint =($\frac{1}{2}$ quart)/ 2 quarts   14. 1 gallon = 8 quarts /(4 quarts)

15. 3 quarts =(12 cups)/ 6 cups   16. 1 quart = $\frac{1}{2}$ gallon /($\frac{1}{4}$ gallon)

Estimating and Comparing Weight

The **ounce (oz)** and **pound (lb)** are customary units for measuring weight. Thinking about objects that weigh about 1 ounce or 1 pound can help you estimate the weight of other objects.

A large strawberry weighs about 1 ounce. A soccer ball weighs about 1 pound.

Complete each sentence. Write *more* or *less*.

1. A paper clip weighs ____**less**____ than 1 ounce.

2. A cat weighs ____**more**____ than 1 pound.

3. An egg weighs ____**more**____ than 1 ounce.

4. A penny weighs ____**less**____ than 1 ounce.

5. A watermelon weighs ____**more**____ than 1 pound.

6. A chalkboard eraser weighs ____**less**____ than 1 pound.

Write the unit of measure you would use to weigh each object. Write *ounce* or *pound*.

7.
____**lb**____

8.
____**oz**____

9.
____**lb**____

10.
____**lb**____

11.
____**oz**____

12.
____**oz**____

Harcourt Brace School Publishers

Centimeter, Decimeter, Meter

Centimeter (c), **decimeter (dm)**, and **meter (m)** are units used to measure length or distance.

This line is 1 centimeter (cm) long.

├──┤

100 of these lines placed end to end equal 1 meter (m).
100 cm = 1 m

This line is 1 decimeter (dm) long.

├────────────────┤

10 of these lines placed end to end equal 1 meter (m).
10 dm = 1 m

---

1. Which unit would you use to measure the length of an ant?

   a. Is an ant large, small, or somewhere in between? ____small____

   b. Which unit would use to measure something small? ____cm____

   c. Which unit would you use to measure the ant? ____cm____

   d. Why wouldn't you use a meter to measure the ant?

   ____Possible answer: The unit is larger than the ant.____

2. Which unit would you use to measure the length of a bird?

   a. Is a bird large, small, or somewhere in between? ____in between____

   b. Which unit would you use to measure the bird? ____dm____

   c. Why wouldn't you use a meter to measure the bird?

   ____Possible answer: The unit is larger than the bird.____

Choose the unit that you would use to measure each.
Write *cm, dm,* or *m.*

3. ladybug ____cm____

4. horse ____m____

5. rabbit ____dm____

Estimating and Comparing Length

- The width of your index finger is about 1 cm.
- The width of an adult's hand is about 1 dm.
- Your arm is about 1 m long.

1. Record your estimate of the length of each object in the table. Then measure each object to the nearest whole unit and record. **Estimates and actual measurements will vary. Check students' tables.**

Object	Unit	Estimate	Measurement
Sneaker	dm		
Chalkboard	m		
Watch	dm		
Classmate's finger	cm		
Your classroom	m		
Penny	cm		
Crayon	cm		
Flag	dm		
Classmate's arm	m		

2. Order the items in your list from shortest to longest.

_____ **Possible order: penny, finger, crayon,**

_____ **watch, sneaker, flag, arm,**

_____ **chalkboard, classroom**

_____

Harcourt Brace School Publishers

Measuring and Drawing Length

Jan needs to draw a 5-cm line to begin a sketch of her room. How can she use her ruler to draw this line?

Step 1

Place the ruler where you want to draw the line.

Step 2

Draw a dot by the left edge, or the zero mark, of the ruler.

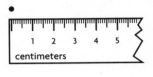

Step 3

Draw a dot above the 5 mark on the ruler.

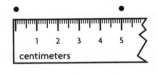

Step 4

Draw a line connecting the dots.

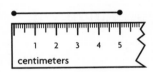

---

1. Bob needs to draw a line that is 12 cm long. The steps he should follow are listed below. Arrange the steps in order by writing 1, 2, 3, and 4 in the blanks.

   ___3___ **a.** Draw a dot above the 12 mark on the ruler.

   ___2___ **b.** Draw a dot by the left edge or the zero mark.

   ___1___ **c.** Place the ruler where you want to draw the line.

   ___4___ **d.** Draw a line connecting the two dots.

2. Draw a line 8 cm long.
   Check students' drawings.

3. Draw a line 4 cm long.
   Check students' drawings.

4. Draw an eraser 7 cm long.
   Check students' drawings.

5. Draw a key 6 cm long.
   Check students' drawings.

Problem-Solving Strategy

Work Backward

Tiko spent 4 days building a 98-cm bridge out of craft sticks and toothpicks. He built 24 cm of the bridge on Tuesday, 29 cm of the bridge on Wednesday, and 27 cm on Thursday. How much of the bridge did Tiko build on Monday?

UNDERSTAND

1. What are you asked to do? _____ <u>to find how much of</u>

_____<u>the bridge Tiko built on Monday</u>_____

2. What information will you use? _____ <u>the bridge's length; 24 cm</u>

_____<u>on Tuesday, 29 cm on Wednesday,</u>_____

_____<u>and 27 cm on Thursday</u>_____

PLAN

3. What strategy can you use to solve the problem?

_____<u>work backward</u>_____

SOLVE

4. How can you work backward to solve the problem?

_____<u>add the lengths built on Tuesday, Wednesday, and</u>

_____<u>Thursday; subtract the total from the total length</u>

_____<u>of the bridge</u>_____

5. How much of the bridge did he build on Monday?

_____<u>18 cm</u>_____

6. What other strategy could you use?

_____<u>Possible answers: Make a model or act it out.</u>

Harcourt Brace School Publishers

Estimating and Comparing Capacity

Capacity is the amount a container will hold when it is filled. Capacity can be measured using the metric units **milliliter (mL)** and **liter (L)**.

1,000 mL = 1L

---

1. Tanya needs to put 6,000 mL of water into a tub. How many 1 L jugs should she fill?

   a. How many milliliters equal 1 liter? _____ **1,000 mL** _____

   b. How many liters equal 1,000 milliliters? _____ **1 L** _____

   c. How many milliliters of water does Tanya need to put in the tub? _____ **6,000 mL** _____

   d. How many liter containers should she fill? _____ **6** _____

2. Roy needs to put 4 liters of juice into a cooler. He has a container that holds 500 mL. How many containers of juice should he put into the cooler?

   a. How many milliliters equal 1 liter? _____ **1,000 mL** _____

   b. How many milliliters equal 4 liters? _____ **4,000 mL** _____

   c. How many groups of 500 are in 4,000? _____ **8** _____

   d. How many containers of juice does he need? _____ **8** _____

3. The soccer coach has 8 L of sports drink. He wants to pour the drink into bottles that hold 1,000 mL each. How many bottles does he need?

   a. How many milliliters equal 1 liter? _____ **1,000 mL** _____

   b. How many milliliters equal 8 liters? _____ **8,000 mL** _____

   c. How many groups of 1,000 mL are in 8 L? _____ **8** _____

   d. How many bottles does he need? _____ **8** _____

Estimating and Comparing Mass

The metric units for measuring mass are **gram (g)** and **kilogram (kg)**.

$$1,000 \text{ g} = 1 \text{ kg}$$

---

1. A box has a mass of 7 kg. What is the mass of the box in grams?

   a. How many grams equal 1 kilogram? _____1,000 g_____

   b. What is the mass of the box in kilograms? _____7 kg_____

   c. How many grams equal 7 kg? _____7,000 g_____

   d. What is the mass of the box in grams? _____7,000 g_____

2. A stack of books has a mass of 9,000 grams. What is the mass of the books in kilograms?

   a. How many grams equal 1 kilogram? _____1,000 g_____

   b. What is the mass of the books in grams? _____9,000 g_____

   c. How many kilograms equal 9,000 grams? _____9 kg_____

   d. What is the mass of the books in kilograms? _____9 kg_____

3. A suitcase has a mass of 12,000 grams. What is the mass of the suitcase in kilograms?

   a. How many grams equal 1 kilogram? _____1,000 g_____

   b. How many groups of 1,000 are in 12,000? _____12_____

   c. How many kilograms equal 12,000 grams? _____12 kg_____

   d. What is the mass of the suitcase in kilograms? _____12 kg_____

4. A cat has a mass of 5 kg. What is the mass of the cat in grams? _____5,000 g_____

Harcourt Brace School Publishers

Finding Perimeter

Perimeter is the distance around a plane figure.

Jack used unit cubes to measure
the perimeter of a photograph of
his cat. He needed 16 unit cubes
to go all the way around the photograph.

The perimeter of the photograph is 16 cubes.

Find the perimeter of each figure. You may use unit cubes.

1.

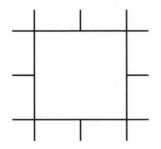

_____ 8 cubes _____

2.

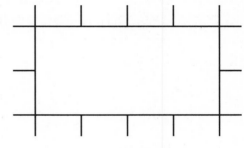

_____ 12 cubes _____

3.

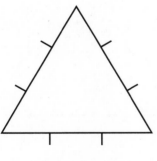

_____ 9 cubes _____

4.

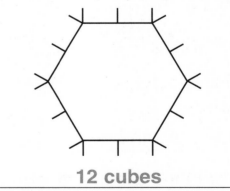

_____ 12 cubes _____

5.

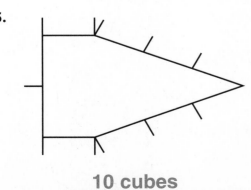

_____ 10 cubes _____

6.

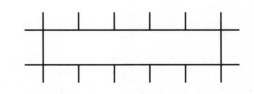

_____ 12 cubes _____

Name _____

More About Perimeter

Perimeter is the distance around a plane figure. You can add the lengths of the sides of a figure to find the perimeter.

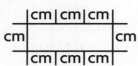

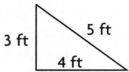

1 cm + 3 cm + 1 cm + 3 cm = 8 cm

The perimeter is 8 centimeters.

3 ft + 4 ft + 5 ft = 12 ft

The perimeter is 12 feet.

Use a centimeter ruler to measure the length of each side. Then add the sides to find the perimeter.

1.

3 cm + 3 cm + 3 cm + 3 cm

= 12 cm

2.

2 cm + 6 cm + 2 cm + 6 cm

= 16 cm

3.

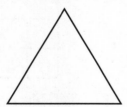

3 cm + 3 cm + 3 cm

= 9 cm

4.

5 cm + 2 cm + 3 cm + 2 cm

= 12 cm

Find the perimeter of each figure.

5.

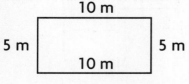

30 m

6.

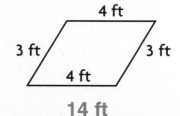

14 ft

7.

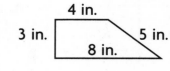

20 in.

R148   TAKE ANOTHER LOOK

Finding Area

The **area** of a figure is the number of square units
needed to cover a flat surface.

This is a
square unit.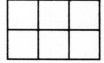

Count or skip-count the number
of square units to find the area. The
area of the figure is 6 square units.

Count or skip-count to find the area. Tell how many
square units are in each figure.

1.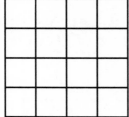

_____ **16 sq units** _____

2.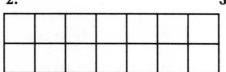

_____ **14 sq units** _____

3.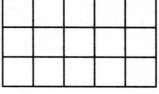

_____ **15 sq units** _____

4.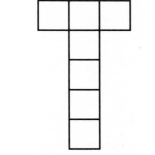

_____ **7 sq units** _____

5.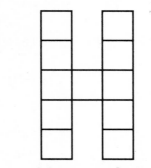

_____ **11 sq units** _____

6.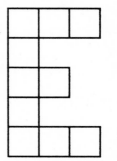

_____ **10 sq units** _____

7.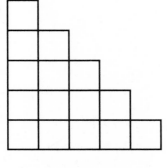

_____ **15 sq units** _____

8.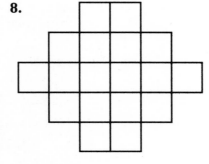

_____ **18 sq units** _____

9.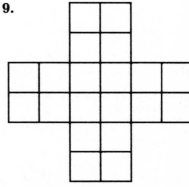

_____ **20 sq units** _____

Name _____

Perimeter and Area

Meg is thinking of different ways to sew together
12 quilt squares to make a wall hanging. She plans to
sew a ribbon around the border of the wall hanging.
Which wall hanging has the greatest perimeter?

Find the area by counting the number of square units.

Find the perimeter by adding the lengths of each side.

    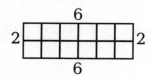   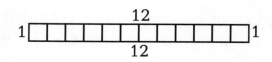

area = 12 square units   area = 12 square units   area = 12 square units
perimeter = 14 units   perimeter = 16 units   perimeter = 26 units

The long, narrow wall hanging has the greatest perimeter.

Find the area and perimeter of each figure.

1.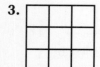

   area = __8__ sq units

   perimeter = __12__ units

2.

   area = __8__ sq units

   perimeter = __18__ units

3.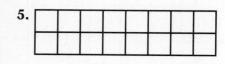

   area = __9__ sq units

   perimeter = __12__ units

4.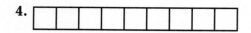

   area = __9__ sq units

   perimeter = __20__ units

5.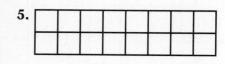

   area = __16__ sq units

   perimeter = __20__ units

6.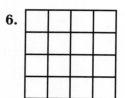

   area = __16__ sq units

   perimeter = __16__ units

Name _____

Problem-Solving Strategy

Act It Out

Matthew has 12 yards of fencing. He wants to make a pen for his chicks. Which pen has the greatest area?

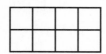

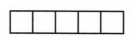

perimeter = 12 yd
area = 9 sq yd

perimeter = 12 yd
area = 8 sq yd

perimeter = 12 yd
area = 5 sq yd

The pen with the largest area is a square with 3 yards on each side.

___

Find the perimeter and area of each figure.

1. perimeter = __10__ units

   area = __6__ sq units

2. perimeter = __10__ units

   area = __4__ sq units

3. perimeter = __8__ units

   area = __4__ sq units

4. perimeter = __8__ units

   area = __3__ sq units

5. Draw 3 different rectangles that each have a perimeter of 14 units. Circle the rectangle with the greatest area. **Check students' drawings and circles.**

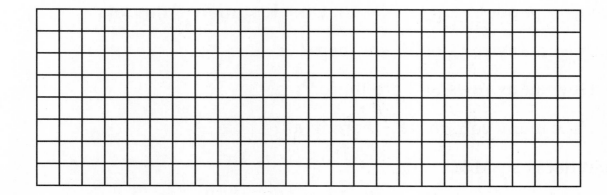

Arrays with Tens and Ones

You can use grid paper to help you multiply.

Example 3×12

- Draw a rectangle with 3 rows and 12 columns on grid paper.

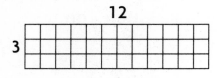

- Draw a line after the tenth column to make two rectangles.

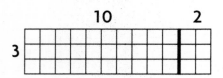

- There are 3 rows of 10. $3 \times 10 = 30$
- There are 3 rows of 2. $3 \times 2 = 6$
- There are 36 squares in all. $30 + 6 = 36$
- $3 \times 12 = 36$

---

1. Use grid paper to model 4×11. **Check students' models.**

   a. How many rows of 10 are there? ___4___

   b. How many rows of 1 are there? ___4___

   c. How many squares are there in all? ___44___

   d. What is 4×11? ___44___

2. Use grid paper to model 5×13. **Check students' models.**

   a. How many rows of 10 are there? ___5___

   b. How many rows of 3 are there? ___5___

   c. How many squares are there in all? ___65___

   d. What is 5×13? ___65___

3. Use grid paper to help you find 6×18. ___108___

Harcourt Brace School Publishers

Problem-Solving Strategy

Make a Model

Making a model often helps you see the information.

Tanya collects sea shells. She arranges her shells in
3 rows, with 18 shells in each row. How many shells
does Tanya have?

Step 1 Make a model
on grid paper.

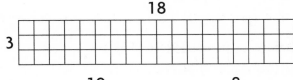

18
3

Step 2 Use the model to
multiply the tens
and the ones.

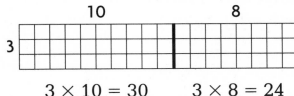

10   8
3

$3 \times 10 = 30$ $3 \times 8 = 24$

Step 3 Find the total
number of squares.

$30 + 24 = 54$

So, Tanya has 54 shells.

Make a model. Then solve. Check students' models.

1. Molly made cookies. She
placed the cookies in 2 rows
of 16 to cool. How many
cookies did she bake?

   _____ **32 cookies** _____

2. Daniel has a collection of toy
race cars. He puts them on
the floor in 2 rows of 18. How
many race cars does he have?

   _____ **36 race cars** _____

3. Marty's Market has 6 shelves
of cereal boxes. Each shelf
has 13 cereal boxes. How
many cereal boxes in all does
Marty's Market have?

   _____ **78 boxes of cereal** _____

4. Sally has a garden. In her
garden she has 4 rows of
flowers. Each row has
13 flowers in it. How many
flowers does she have in
her garden?

   _____ **52 flowers** _____

Modeling Multiplication

$3 \times 16 =$ __?__

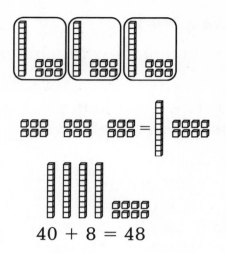

- Show 3 groups of 16 with base-ten blocks.

- Take the ones, and regroup them to make ten. There is 1 new group of ten, plus 8 ones.

- Put all the tens together. You now have 4 sets of tens and 8 ones.

- $3 \times 16 = 48$

$40 + 8 = 48$

Look at the problems below. Regroup the model and draw. Then complete the number sentence.

Model   **Regroup**

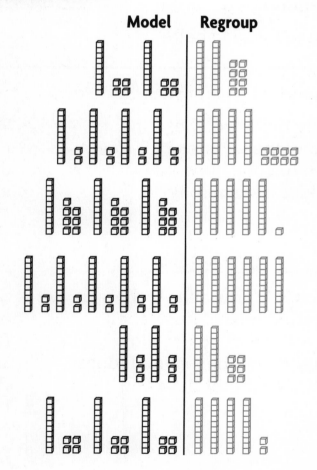

1. $2 \times 14 =$ __?__

   ___28___

2. $4 \times 12 =$ __?__

   ___48___

3. $3 \times 17 =$ __?__

   ___51___

4. $5 \times 12 =$ __?__

   ___60___

5. $2 \times 13 =$ __?__

   ___26___

6. $3 \times 14 =$ __?__

   ___42___

Recording Multiplication

Example   24
     $\times\ 3$

- Multiply the ones.

$$\begin{array}{r} 4 \\ \times\ 3 \\ \hline 12 \end{array}$$

- Multiply the tens.

$$\begin{array}{r} 20 \\ \times\ 3 \\ \hline 60 \end{array}$$

- Record the products under the original problem.
- Add the two products.

$$\begin{array}{r} 24 \\ \times\ 3 \\ \hline 12\ \leftarrow \text{ product of ones} \\ +60\ \leftarrow \text{ product of tens} \\ \hline 72\ \leftarrow \text{ total} \end{array}$$

Find the product. Use a model to help you.

1.
$$\begin{array}{r} 13 \\ \times\ 2 \\ \hline 6\ \leftarrow \text{ product of ones} \\ +20\ \leftarrow \text{ product of tens} \\ \hline 26 \end{array}$$

2.
$$\begin{array}{r} 23 \\ \times\ 4 \\ \hline 12\ \leftarrow \text{ product of ones} \\ +80\ \leftarrow \text{ product of tens} \\ \hline 92 \end{array}$$

3.
$$\begin{array}{r} 15 \\ \times\ 3 \\ \hline 15\ \leftarrow \text{ product of ones} \\ +30\ \leftarrow \text{ product of tens} \\ \hline 45 \end{array}$$

4.
$$\begin{array}{r} 16 \\ \times\ 5 \\ \hline 30\ \leftarrow \text{ product of ones} \\ +50\ \leftarrow \text{ product of tens} \\ \hline 80 \end{array}$$

5.
$$\begin{array}{r} 12 \\ \times\ 3 \\ \hline 6\ \leftarrow \text{ product of ones} \\ +30\ \leftarrow \text{ product of tens} \\ \hline 36 \end{array}$$

6.
$$\begin{array}{r} 22 \\ \times\ 5 \\ \hline 10\ \leftarrow \text{ product of ones} \\ +100\ \leftarrow \text{ product of tens} \\ \hline 110 \end{array}$$

7.
$$\begin{array}{r} 32 \\ \times\ 4 \\ \hline 128 \end{array}$$

8.
$$\begin{array}{r} 25 \\ \times\ 4 \\ \hline 100 \end{array}$$

9.
$$\begin{array}{r} 36 \\ \times\ 5 \\ \hline 180 \end{array}$$

Practicing Multiplication

Example $4 \times 38 = \underline{\ ?\ }$

- Rewrite as:

$$\begin{array}{r} 38 \\ \times\ 4 \\ \hline \end{array}$$

- Multiply the ones. $4 \times 8 = 32$ ones

- Regroup 32 ones as 3 tens 2 ones.

- Write the 2 under the ones and the 3 over the tens.

tens	ones
$\overset{3}{3}$	8
$\times$	4
	2

- Multiply the tens. $4 \times 3 = 12$ tens

- Add the 3 tens you regrouped. $12 + 3 = 15$ tens

- Regroup 15 tens as 1 hundred 5 tens.

- Write the 5 under the tens and the 1 in the hundreds column.

hundreds	tens	ones
	$\overset{3}{3}$	8
$\times$		4
1	5	2

Complete each problem below. You may use base-ten blocks to help you.

1. $\begin{array}{r} 18 \\ \times\ 3 \\ \hline 54 \end{array}$

2. $\begin{array}{r} 36 \\ \times\ 2 \\ \hline 72 \end{array}$

3. $\begin{array}{r} 55 \\ \times\ 5 \\ \hline 275 \end{array}$

4. $\begin{array}{r} 61 \\ \times\ 4 \\ \hline 244 \end{array}$

5. $\begin{array}{r} 27 \\ \times\ 4 \\ \hline 108 \end{array}$

6. $\begin{array}{r} 14 \\ \times\ 7 \\ \hline 98 \end{array}$

7. $\begin{array}{r} 32 \\ \times\ 6 \\ \hline 192 \end{array}$

8. $\begin{array}{r} 17 \\ \times\ 2 \\ \hline 34 \end{array}$

9. $\begin{array}{r} 12 \\ \times\ 8 \\ \hline 96 \end{array}$

10. $\begin{array}{r} 63 \\ \times\ 6 \\ \hline 378 \end{array}$

11. $\begin{array}{r} 45 \\ \times\ 4 \\ \hline 180 \end{array}$

12. $\begin{array}{r} 52 \\ \times\ 5 \\ \hline 260 \end{array}$

13. $\begin{array}{r} 78 \\ \times\ 7 \\ \hline 546 \end{array}$

14. $\begin{array}{r} 26 \\ \times\ 6 \\ \hline 156 \end{array}$

15. $\begin{array}{r} 94 \\ \times\ 3 \\ \hline 282 \end{array}$

16. $\begin{array}{r} 23 \\ \times\ 3 \\ \hline 69 \end{array}$

Harcourt Brace School Publishers

Dividing with Remainders

Sometimes you cannot divide objects evenly into groups.

Find 14 ÷ 4.

Use 14 counters

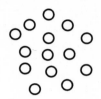

Draw 4 circles. Divide the 14 counters into
4 equal groups by putting them in the circles.

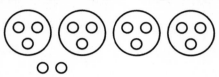

The **quotient** is 3—the number of counters in each of 4 groups.
The **remainder** is 2—the number of leftover counters.

Write: 14 ÷ 4 = 3 r2

Use the picture to find the quotient and remainder.

1. 11 ÷ 2 = ___5 r1___   ⬭⬭⬭⬭⬭ ⬭⬭⬭⬭⬭ ○

2. 9 ÷ 4 = ___2 r1___   ⬭ ⬭⬭ ⬭⬭ ⬭⬭ ⬭ ○

3. 13 ÷ 3 = ___4 r1___   ⬭⬭⬭⬭ ⬭⬭⬭⬭ ⬭⬭⬭⬭ ○

4. 11 ÷ 4 = ___2 r3___   ⬭ ⬭⬭ ⬭⬭ ⬭⬭ ⬭ ○ ○ ○

Find the quotient and remainder. You may use counters to
help you.

5. 12 ÷ 5 = ___2 r2___   **6.** 10 ÷ 3 = ___3 r1___   **7.** 9 ÷ 2 = ___4 r1___

8. 13 ÷ 2 = ___6 r1___   **9.** 15 ÷ 4 = ___3 r3___   **10.** 8 ÷ 3 = ___2 r2___

11. 10 ÷ 4 = ___2 r2___   **12.** 7 ÷ 3 = ___2 r1___   **13.** 17 ÷ 3 = ___5 r2___

14. 11 ÷ 3 = ___3 r2___   **15.** 16 ÷ 5 = ___3 r1___   **16.** 5 ÷ 3 = ___1 r2___

Modeling Division

Divide 74 into 3 equal groups.

Write: 74 ÷ 3 = ___?___

Step 1	Step 2
Show 74 as 7 tens and 4 ones. Draw 3 circles to show 3 groups.	Begin by dividing the 7 tens. Place an equal number of tens into each circle.
Step 3	**Step 4**
There are now 2 tens in each circle. Regroup the 1 ten left over into ones. Now there are 14 ones.	Divide the 14 ones. Place an equal number of ones in each circle.

There are 2 tens and 4 ones in each circle. There are 2 ones left over.

So, 74 ÷ 3 = 24 r2.

Find the quotient. Use base-ten blocks to model each problem.

1. 35 ÷ 2 = __17 r1__   2. 35 ÷ 3 = __11 r2__   3. 35 ÷ 4 = __8 r3__

4. 67 ÷ 2 = __33 r1__   5. 67 ÷ 3 = __22 r1__   6. 67 ÷ 4 = __16 r3__

7. 45 ÷ 2 = __22 r1__   8. 45 ÷ 3 = __15__   9. 45 ÷ 4 = __11 r1__

Harcourt Brace School Publishers

Recording Division

Divide 93 into 4 equal groups.

Write: $93 \div 4 = $ _?_ and $4\overline{)93}^{?}$

Step 1	Step 2
Show 93 as 9 tens and 3 ones. Draw 4 circles to show 4 groups.	Begin by dividing the 9 tens. Place an equal number of tens into each circle. $\quad$ 2 ← 2 tens in $4\overline{)93}\quad$ each group $\underline{-8}$ ← 8 tens used $\quad$ 1 ← 1 ten left

Step 3	Step 4	Step 5
Regroup the 1 ten left over into ones. Now there are 13 ones. $\quad$ 2 $4\overline{)93}$ $\underline{-8\downarrow}$ $\quad$ 13 ← bring $\qquad$ down $\qquad$ ones	Divide the 13 ones. Place an equal number of ones in each circle. $\quad$ 23 ← 3 ones in $4\overline{)93}\quad$ each group $\underline{-8\downarrow}$ $\quad$ 13 $\underline{-12}$ ← 12 ones used $\qquad$ 1 ← 1 one left	Record the remainder next to the quotient. $\quad$ 23 r1 $4\overline{)93}$ $\underline{-8}$ $\quad$ 13 $\underline{-12}$ $\qquad$ 1

So, $93 \div 4 = 23$ r1 and $4\overline{)93}^{23\ r1}$.

Use base-ten blocks to model each problem. Record the numbers as you complete each step.

		2	4	r1			1	7	r1			1	2	r3			3	5	r1
1. 2)		4	9		2. 3)		5	2		3. 4)		5	1		4. 2)		7	1	
−		4	↓		−		3	↓		−		4	↓		−		6	↓	
		0	9				2	2				1	1				1	1	
−			8		−		2	1		−			8		−		1	0	
			1					1					3					1	

Practicing Division

$63 \div 4 = $ _?_

Remember these steps:
D ivide
M ultiply
S ubtract
C ompare
B ring down

$\begin{array}{r} 1 \\ 4)\overline{63} \\ -\ 4 \\ \hline 2 \end{array}$	**D**ivide the tens **Multiply** $\quad 4 \times 1 = 4$ **Subtract** $\quad 6 - 4 = 2$ **Compare** $\quad 2 < 4$
$\begin{array}{r} 1 \\ 4)\overline{63} \\ -\ 4\downarrow \\ \hline 23 \end{array}$	**Bring down the ones**
$\begin{array}{r} 15 \\ 4)\overline{63} \\ -\ 4\downarrow \\ \hline 23 \\ -\ 20 \\ \hline 3 \end{array}$	**D**ivide the ones **Multiply** $\quad 4 \times 5 = 20$ **Subtract** $\quad 23 - 20 = 3$ **Compare** $\quad 3 < 4$
$\begin{array}{r} 15\ r3 \\ 4)\overline{63} \\ -\ 4\downarrow \\ \hline 23 \\ -\ 20 \\ \hline 3 \end{array}$	**Bring down?** There is nothing left to bring down. If there is a remainder, record it next to the quotient.

Find the quotient. Use the D, M, S, C, and B steps above.

1. $\begin{array}{r} 3\ \ 6\ \ r1 \\ 2)\overline{7\ \ 3} \\ -\ 6\downarrow \\ \hline 1\ \ 3 \\ -\ 1\ \ 2 \\ \hline 1 \end{array}$	2. $\begin{array}{r} 1\ \ 2 \\ 5)\overline{6\ \ 0} \\ -\ 5\downarrow \\ \hline 1\ \ 0 \\ -\ 1\ \ 0 \\ \hline 0 \end{array}$	3. $\begin{array}{r} 1\ \ 6\ \ r2 \\ 4)\overline{6\ \ 6} \\ -\ 4\downarrow \\ \hline 2\ \ 6 \\ -\ 2\ \ 4 \\ \hline 2 \end{array}$	4. $\begin{array}{r} 2\ \ 5 \\ 3)\overline{7\ \ 5} \\ -\ 6\downarrow \\ \hline 1\ \ 5 \\ -\ 1\ \ 5 \\ \hline 0 \end{array}$

Choosing Multiplication or Division

Multiply:

- When you are joining groups of equal size.

- When you know the size of the groups and the number of groups.

Example: Josh has 4 decks of playing cards. Each deck has 52 cards. How many cards does Josh have in all?

$4 \times 52 = 208$

Josh has 208 cards.

Divide:

- When you are separating a total into groups of equal size.

- When you know the total.

- When you know either the number of groups **or** the number in each group.

Example: There are 4 children who are sharing a deck of 52 playing cards. How many cards does each child get?

$52 \div 4 = 13$

Each child gets 13 cards.

Write whether you would multiply or divide. Then solve.

1. Mr. Davis drives 26 miles each day. How many miles does he drive in 5 days?

   _____multiply; 130 mi_____

2. Felix baked 48 cookies. He put 3 cookies into each bag. How many bags did he use?

   _____divide; 16 bags_____

3. The Watkins family buys 4 pairs of skates. Each pair of skates costs $29. How much money do they spend in all?

   _____multiply; $116_____

4. Maria read 85 pages in 5 days. She read the same number of pages daily. How many pages did she read each day?

   _____divide; 17 pages_____

5. There are 42 students traveling in 3 vans. The same number of students are riding in each van. How many students are in each van?

   _____divide; 14 students_____

6. There are 3 classes visiting the library. There are 26 students in each class. How many students in all are visiting the library?

   _____multiply; 78 students_____

Problem-Solving Strategy

Write a Number Sentence

You can write a number sentence to help you solve a problem.

Examples:

There are 27 students in Amy's class. They are working in groups of 3. How many groups are there?

$$27 \div 3 = 9$$

number of students · number in each group · number of groups

There are 3 classes going on a field trip together. There are 27 students in each class. How many students in all are going on the field trip?

$$3 \times 27 = 81$$

number of classes · number of students in each class · total number of students

---

Write a number sentence to solve. Then write the answer.

1. Brad has 65 CDs. He puts the same number of CDs on each shelf. There are 5 shelves. How many CDs does he put on each shelf?

   $65 \div 5 = 13;$

   13 CDs

2. Mr. Turner is writing math problems for his class. He writes 5 pages of math problems. Each page has 18 problems. How many problems does he write in all?

   $5 \times 18 = 90;$

   90 problems

3. There are 24 cabins at the camp. There are 8 bunk beds in each cabin. How many bunk beds are there in all?

   $24 \times 8 = 192;$

   192 bunk beds

4. It takes Jake about 5 minutes to make a card. About how many cards can Jake make in 60 minutes?

   $60 \div 5 = 12;$

   12 cards

Harcourt Brace School Publishers